practical
CLASSICS
& Car Restorer
ON
METALWORKING
IN
RESTORATION

Reprinted from
Practical Classics magazine

ISBN 1 869826 396

Published by
Brooklands Books with the permission of *Practical Classics*

practical CLASSICS

Distributed by:
Brooklands Book Distribution Ltd.,
Holmerise, Seven Hills Road,
Cobham, Surrey KT11 1ES,
England.   Tel: 09326 5051

Motorbooks International,
Osceola,
Wisconsin 54020 U.S.A.
Tel: 715 294 3345

Printed in Hong Kong

practical CLASSICS

CONTENTS

INTRODUCTION

Practical Classics has been the only motoring magazine to tackle the restoration of automotive bodywork in depth. This book represents a major work on metalworking as applied to car restoration and as such is likely to prove an invaluable asset to every D-I-Y restoration enthusiast. It covers from the very basics, such as how to choose your metal, right up to the skills and techniques of panel fabricating and panel beating.

It also includes an article on reproduction panels, which although it is hardly a D-I-Y feature, does cover a very important area of automotive metalworking and is one of the best articles ever written on the subject.

Michael Brisby brought his many years experience in the restoration trade to his excellent articles on panel beating and on the making of repair panels, while Steve Demol as a highly qualified sheet metal worker and welder was the sheet anchor and font of much of the wisdom that appears in the very detailed metalworking series that ran from June 1985 to October 1986.

Practical Classics was fully involved in the revolution which MIG welding brought to the car restoration hobby. When the smaller MIG welders first appeared at under £200, making them accessible to the D-I-Y enthusiast, the *Practical Classics* report by Steve Demol was taken to heart by a leading British manufacturer. As a result Steve's comments led to a 'mini' MIG which incorporated a 'non-live' torch and automatic wire feed. Other manufacturers followed suit and within months MIG welding, with its virtues of minimum heat distortion and ease of use, has become firmly established as the most popular form of welding for the D-I-Y enthusiast. However the part that can still be played by arc, carbon arc, spot and gas welding has not been overlooked and these porcesses are all covered in articles in this book.

Metalworking

If there is one experience which bonds pretty well all classic car enthusiasts together, it is that sickening moment when you realise that, even though you have been reading *Practical Classics* for more than three years, even though you have joined the relevant one-make car club and have been diligently studying the buying guides, you have STILL allowed your heart to rule your wallet and have bought a car which needs more body work than you know how to do. Placing your head between your knees will relieve the nausea. Learning some basic metalwork, however, will be of longer-term benefit.

Although articles on the more advanced techniques appear in *Practical Classics* from time to time, there are a number basic principals of metal craft which newcomers to the 'sport' should know – the *most* basic of which is that you should be working the right materials with the right tools. Here then is your first obstacle: What sort of metal do you need and where on earth do you buy it?

Materials

The stockist will normally keep a good range of gauges. Be sure you know what thickness you need before you visit the store.

The vast majority of post-war cars have bodies made from pressed steel and you can buy steel in flat sheets, although establishing a source is something of a problem.

There are some vehicle restorers, professional as well as DIY, who use nothing but steel from scrap panels cut out of derelict vehicles. They claim this is cheaper than buying new steel. It might be, but consider the effort required to chisel out the required piece, think of the jagged edges putting your skin, clothes and car carpets (when transporting it home) at risk. Think of the work needed to trim the edges properly and deal with any distortion.

Scrap metal from an old car will be painted and may just have underseal on it. The paint will have to be removed before welding and if you have scribed a line on paintwork it will be lost as soon as a you start to bend the metal. Undersealed panels are best left well alone. About the only advantage a scrap panel might give you is a useful curve or fold which you might be able to incorporate in your repair. For the purposes of this article, then, we will be looking at working new sheet steel. Once

Steel stockists hold sheet metal in pieces measuring about 4ft x 8ft.

Back to basics with Geoff Le Prevost

Metalworking

A sheet this size will replace quite of lot of rotten bodywork and will set you back about £7-£8.

Files should always be fitted with a handle — one slip and that tang becomes a deadly weapon which is about to assault your wrist.

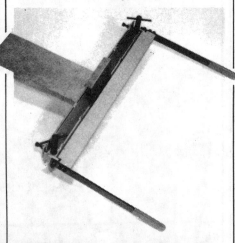

A metal folder is very useful if a number of bends have to be put into the steel — if replacing 'top hat' sections for instance. The steel stockist we spoke to was quite prepared to do this sort of work for the enthusiast who could provide the dimensions – at a very reasonable cost.

The joddler or edge setter in action. It takes quite a hefty 'squeeze' to set an edge and a first timer might try taking only small 'bites', perhaps only half of the width of the jaws each time. A bodywork man would probably recomend that the larger piece of steel (perhaps a car wing) should be joddled, not the repair panel.

you have located the raw material, I think you will be surprised at how inexpensive it is compared with the effort involved with scrap.

Steel stock-holders are difficult to locate simply because they have company names like 'Bloggs & Co.' Try looking in the yellow pages under Sheet Metal Stockists and if you have no joy, try the section headed Steel Merchants – see Iron and Steel Merchants and Importers.

We took a shortcut and asked a friendly local bodywork man where he got his supplies of steel and he put us on to General Assemblies, of Canon Road, Bromley, which turned out to be a friendly and helpful company with staff who are happy to cut as much – or as little – sheet steel as your require.

Having found your stockist, what do you ask for? Sheet steel comes in various thicknesses measured in units of Standard Wire Gauge (SWG) and usually referred to as just 'gauge'. The smaller the gauge number, the thicker the steel. Car bodies are normally made from several different gauges of steel. The body panels and floors are usually 20 or 22 gauge which is relatively thin, while the chassis of an older car would have been the comparatively thick 12 or 14 gauge. Box sections on a more modern car would probably be 16 or 18 gauge.

Galvanised steel might sound like a good idea, but you do need to remove the protective coating to weld it. The fumes are very toxic. If you scratch the coating off, rust will set in very quickly. If you store ordinary sheet steel for a while, keep it in a dry place and leave the protective film of oil on it. Steel usually has sharp edges, so be careful where you leave it.

If the bodywork of your car is aluminium, similar principles apply. The chassis will be in heavy steel but the body panels will in aluminium of a slightly heavier gauge than a similar panel in steel would have been – perhaps 16 or 18 gauge.

Metalworking tools

Your basic requirements will be tools to measure, mark and cut steel with. To start with you will need a ruler. A six inch will not be a lot of use, nor will a six foot flexible steel tape. A steel rule of about two feet will be a good investment. Look after it, you will use if for measuring, scribing straight lines and checking flat surfaces. If you have been tempted to use it as a crowbar or a light hammer, its subsequent usefulness might be impaired.

When marking lines on steel, the tool to use is a scriber. The tip of a screwdriver, or even a suitable nail, if correctly used, is just as effective. An engineer would probably make a series of dots along the scribed line using a dot punch which has a sharper tip than the centre punch used for marking where a hole should be drilled.

Another fairly essential tool is a try square or engineers' square to mark right angles – and to check that they are still right angles when the cut has been made! Squares are made in various sizes and one with a five or six inch blade would probably be sufficient. A combination square, in which the head slides up and down a 12in rule perhaps can be a little bit more useful. They often incorporate a small scriber in the sliding head.

There are a great number of cutting tools available and it is often difficult for a beginner to make a first choice. If you intend doing more than one or two cuts in sheet metal then a decent pair of tin snips will be a good bet. Go for a pair with long handles which will give good leverage, and when you are cutting, don't use the full length of the blade – just make short snips. Using the full length of the blade will produce small nicks at the end

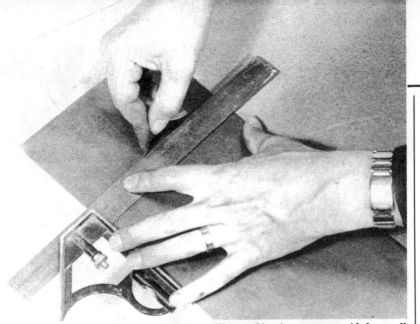

The first stage in preparing the work is to mark it out. This combination square provided a small scriber, but a carefully used screwdriver blade would suffice. Be accurate at this stage, a mistake here could produce a beautifully finished piece of scrap.

A sheet metal cutter of this type is certainly easier to use, but again, some practice is needed before accurate cuts can be made.

Tin snips are an essential part of sheet metal-working equipment. Learn to use them on pieces of scrap, skill in cutting straight and curved lines can only come with practice. It is certainly harder than an expert would make it look.

of each stroke – try it with a sheet of paper and a pair of scissors! Other useful aids might be a hacksaw and/or a junior hacksaw, and a cold chisel. An engineers' ball pein hammer of about 1-1½ lbs is the type most usually found in the workshop.

Having cut the metal, you will need some tools to work it. A panel beating hammer and a selection of dollies – or perhaps just one universal type – and a slapper will all be useful. A slapper is a tool shaped something like a file but without the teeth. It is laid on the metal and hit with a hammer to flatten irregularities.

A hammer and dolly will come in handy for dressing out any deformity caused by cutting the steel.

One of the most expensive, but most necessary basic item in any workshop is a good vice – the toughest you can afford – mounted on an equally tough bench.

Even when you have gone some way towards mastering the tin snips – and they are not easy to use – you will still find that your work needs filing down. Files are usually sold without a handle. You should fit one, your wrists will appreciate it. Some files are sold with plastic handles already fitted. There is quite a range of cutting grades from dead smooth through smooth, and second cut to bastard. There are also several shapes – flat, round, half round, triangular (three square) and square. Build up a collection if you can.

There are many other tools, enough for years and years of Christmas present lists, which you can add to your collection as and when you feel they will be needed, or you can afford them. There are power cutting tools, angle grinders and others; there are sophisticated metal bending tools and equipment for special tasks, such as the joddler. The basic toolkit, however, will see you through most of the workshop jobs.

Dent Clinic

Michael Brisby says that the only way to learn how to remove dents is to get the right tools and practice.

I was most upset when someone watching me struggle to get some dents out of a badly crumpled wing told me, "The thing about panel beaters is that they are all con-men," but while I cannot agree that there is any confidence trick involved it is a bit of a black art. Getting a dented piece of metal back to its original shape *is* often part skill and experience and part luck.

I have done my fair share of straightening cars and I have watched many skilled body repairers at work and found that most of us have our own methods; none of us seem to agree on how to get the best results and find it difficult to explain exactly what we do! In the end it is the results which count — not how they are achieved. However, there *are* some golden rules — before tackling a repair you have to have the right tools and have the knack of using them, you must have a good eye, and you must think about how the damage was caused before planning how to correct it.

TOOLS

When you think about how much money you can save by beating out one minor dent yourself instead of paying a professional to do the job for you, and that any good tools you buy will last you all your motoring life and can be used for restoration work as well as minor repairs, how can you grudge the cost of buying a few panel beating tools? I have seen people who have kitted themselves out with all sorts of panel beating aids at considerable expense and then found that all they used regularly were a few basic tools, some of which thay could have made for themselves.

Unfortunately there is now very little general demand for panel beating tools and you will find that even the very best tool

suppliers are likely to have only a very limited selection in stock or will look up the relevant sections of the manufacturer's catalogue and show you a picture of what they might be willing to order for you. My advice is that you should not buy hammers or dollies without seeing them and getting the feel of them in your hand (we ARE talking about vehicle body repair dollies!). One way you can "try before you buy" is to find an experienced body repairer and ask him about what tools he

Use your hands and your eyes to evaluate a dent before you decide how to tackle it and throughout the straightening process. If you choose tools that suit you and learn how to use them you do not need a vast selection.

uses and recommends, but be warned — a panel beater will very rarely let you try a hammer or dolly out, they are very personal possessions for a skilled man. Try the hammer and dollies he recommends in your hand and if they feel comfortable take a note of the maker and the number of the tool.

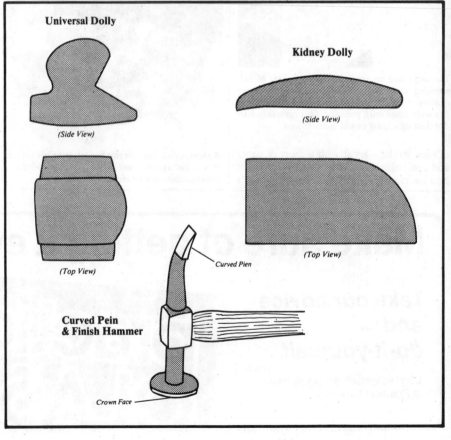

Universal Dolly

(Side View)

(Top View)

Kidney Dolly

(Side View)

(Top View)

Curved Pien

Curved Pein & Finish Hammer

Crown Face

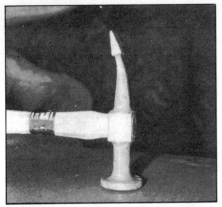

A panel hammer should be used in conjunction with a dolly or a sandbag. The hammer blows should come from the wrist and not the shoulder and arm so that the hammer face strikes the surface of the metal flat.

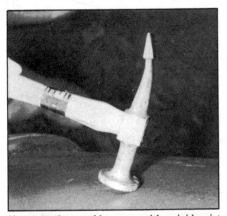

If you use the panel hammer with a rigid wrist it will assume the wrong arc and land like this stretching and marking the metal as it hits.

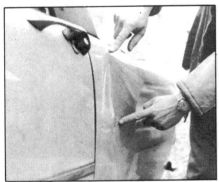

If you go about it the right way this dent on a Rover 2000 rear wing is really quite easy to correct. The point of impact is shown by the lower finger but I would tackle the hard crease at the top of the dent (indicated) first to get rid of the rigidity and greatly increase the chances of the wing springing back into shape with one or two hefty bangs from the suitable dolly with a face that closely matches the shape of the wing.

The principal tools I used when I was actively involved in the trade were a Sykes-Pickavant S-P 537 (catalogue number 053700) curved pein and finish hammer, a Gedore 252 universal dolly and a Gedore 255 kidney dolly. The hammer is a very light well-balanced one weighing only 15 ounces and has a crowned

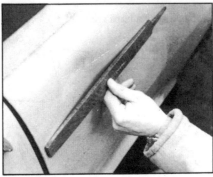

A file is not a straight edge but now the crease at the top of the dent has been softened it helps indicate the extent of the damage and where to "smack" the panel out with the dolly.

On surfaces which should have a regular curvature a new hacksaw blade is a handy guide to the shape you should achieve.

The same dent shown from another angle reveals that the wing of this Morris Series E tourer is in a bad way. In cases like this leave the dents alone until you have removed the wing and repaired the areas which have been weakened by rust. Then refit the wing to get it rigid and deal with the dent.

face — I do not particularly like hammers which are heavy or ones with flat faces. The tools I have mentioned suit *me* but I must stress that they may not suit *you*

A panel hammer should always be used with a wrist movement and very little force is required. If you ever need a big hammer use

one with a soft face or use a suitably shaped piece of flat steel against the panel and strike it with an engineer's hammer. Whatever you strike a panel with must hit the sheet metal squarely or you will stretch and mark it.

EXAMINATION

I have found that no two panel beaters tackle dents the same way and everybody has his own ideas of the "correct" way to do things — and they all write to me to tell me I am wrong!

Presuming that you have the basic panel beating tools along the lines I have suggested — perhaps two or three dollies of different shapes and a good panel hammer — the first step in getting rid of a dent is to examine the damage carefully.

Use your eyes and your hands to determine the nature and extent of the damage and think out how the damage occurred (that is, the point of impact and in what direction rather than an analysis of the accident!). Look at what has to be done' to get proper access to the damage and whether any lamps and bright metal trim will have to come off to prevent damage during what is *supposed* to be a repair exercise! Frequently where wing damage is being tackled it will make life much easier if you remove a wheel but take the trouble to ensure that the car is absolutely securely supported and *cannot* fall before starting work. Certainly any violent pulling or levering should be done with all the wheels on the car.

Proper bumpers were not mounted onto adjacent panels but many post-war cars have the bumper hung on the wings and if it has been driven back into the wing causing a dent it is often worthwhile arranging a steady pull on the bumper and doing the preliminary panel beating on the wing while the strain pulls everything back into position. Once you have the worst of the dents out you can then remove the bumper and straighten or replace it.

METHODS

Every dent is different and only experience can tell you when to use a big hammer and few blows, when to work very gently with a hammer and dolly, which dolly or dolly face to use, when you can use a dolly on its own or in conjunction with a second one and where the use of a sandbag will be better than a dolly.

I am a very firm believer in getting rid of hard creases by turning them into much more gentle bends, even if it means making the dent temporarily deeper before attempting to lift the majority of the dent out with that short series of masterfully executed blows that should, *if* all goes well, spring the dent out almost magically. I usually try to feed metal into the worst area of damage so that by removing all stresses and strains you obtain the "give" to allow the metal to assume its intended shape. To do this I often start by beating out minor dents well back from the damage.

On wings where there is a turned over lip I find that it helps if you remember to correct the shape of the lip as you make progress with

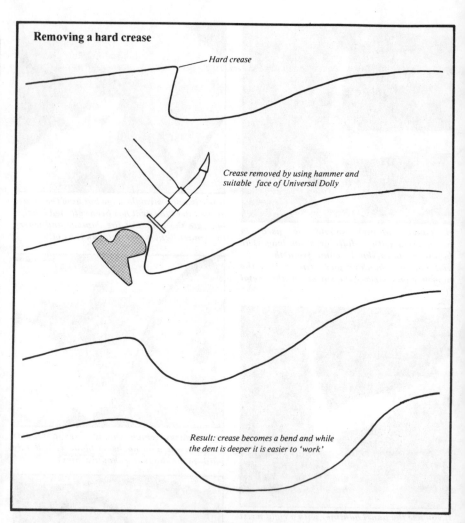

Removing a hard crease

Hard crease

Crease removed by using hammer and suitable face of Universal Dolly

Result: crease becomes a bend and while the dent is deeper it is easier to 'work'

In contrast to the Morris wing a new wing for this Capri is readily available and there is no point in even attempting to beat out the damage. If wings were in short supply it would still be worthwhile looking for a sound secondhand wing to fit rather then attempt the near impossible.

It looks as if the bumper has been driven back on this Renault. In cases like this remove the lights to prevent further damage and put some strain on the bumper which will pull the wing forward with it. Keeping the strain on straighten the wing. Once the main distortion is corrected remove the bumper, the wheel (and the headlamp bowl in some cases) to get proper access to the wing with a hammer and dolly.

the more obvious damage because when the lip is the correct shape it stiffens and holds the shape you want.

DOUBLE SKINNED AREAS

Some of the most difficult dents to deal with occur where the body of the car is double skinned. First a word of warning. If a sill or structural box section is dented you can do some rudimentary straightening (we will go into detail on this subject in another article) but the chances are that the end result will not be perfect and it could be weakened so that in the event of another impact it would be very likely to collapse easily. In such cases once you have done all you can to get the metal straight, cut away the damaged area and weld in a new section (in the case of a sill replace it complete) because you have to *ensure that the vital areas of your car are as strong as the day they left the factory* — unfortunately your life and that of anyone else in the car might depend on it.

Just to keep my hand in I tackled this bumper inflicted damage on the front wing of Joy Ashby's MGB GT. Examination showed that a previous owner had covered up quite a bit of rust but as a short term measure the dent could be removed easily and once it was straightened, the wing would revert to its correct shape above the wheel arch.

HOW DO YOU DO IT?

As I have already stated, no two panel beaters tackle body damage the same way and everybody has his own idea of the "correct" way to do things. On top of that problem a serious dent in an awkward place takes hours to beat out and with a hammer on one side of the panel and a dolly on the other, much of the

It took me half an hour to get to this stage. Most of the work was done with a heavy universal dolly with a second dolly held on the outside in the finishing stages. As the wing came out the wheel arch lip was dressed into shape to hold the correct contour. The next stage would be to weld some small splits, grind them flat and then file the surface of the damaged area to show up the highs and lows which would then be dealt with with a hammer and dolly. When all goes well, no filler is needed.

work is done "blind" which makes photographing a complete repair a major and not very satisfactory undertaking.

As a way round this I have used a selection of photographs of different types of dents and commented upon them in the hope that they will be of some help. □

Metalworking

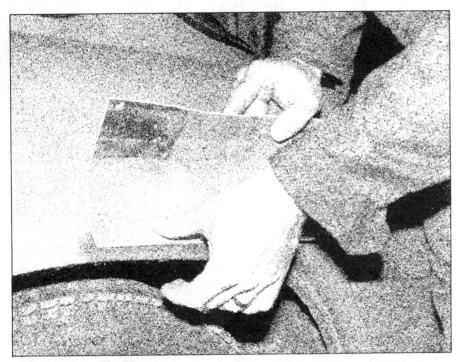

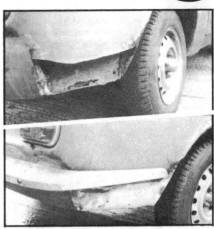

Carrying out bodywork repairs while a vehicle is in regular use can produce some unsightly results but a combination of an adapted Hillman Hunter skirt and a section from a Rover 2000 wing have really blended in quite well on the editor's Alfa.

Michael Brisby demonstrates metalworking techniques making a flared wheel arch repair section

Turning a 90-degree lip on a curved section is not particularly easy. An alternative is to form the panel and the lip as two sections and then weld them together.

Regular readers of *Practical Classics* will know that I am very fond of our Alfa Romeo GT 1600 Junior and that for many months it served as my everyday transport. I think that my wife sometimes grew tired of my enthusiasm for the car until she took it over and now she will not be parted from it — unless the rust gets ahead of us.

Over the past few months I have used whatever spare time I could find to cut out the rotten Italian steel and one of my recent successes has been to replace the rear skirt, below the rear bumper, with a cut down and narrowed panel from a similar area on a Hillman Hunter. I also made up a new lower wing section by adapting a section cut from a sound Rover 2000 rear wing. The reason for my policy of "making do and mending" reflects that if you can get the panels they are a bit more than I can afford, so I have decided that if I save money by cutting out locally

rusted areas, and welding in new metal on the car, I can afford to buy two new front wings. I should imagine that many other enthusiasts who either cannot afford or cannot obtain all new panels probably adopt a similar policy.

As you may have deduced, I have started at the rear of the car and I am working forward and have now reached the rear wheel arches where, as you can see from the photographs, water or condensation has caused rust to form in the double skinned area where the outer wing joins the inner wing. This is a problem common to many, many classic cars and it may not prove possible to find a suitable "donor" panel, so you may well have to make your own repair section.

If the wing edge is a simple matter of a vertical outer surface with a 90-degree lip inwards around the wheel arch, sectioning in a new section, complete with the wheel arch lip, is relatively simple, but there are likely to be two "snags" — forming the lip and avoiding or at least minimising distortion on the wing surface.

Turning a right angle lip in sheet metal is simple enough in a straight line — especially so with a folder like that which we borrowed from C.G. Automation, which produces quick, neat and accurate results. The problem arises when you need to produce a 90-degree lip in a curve.

You can do it by scribing the arc you require and then starting to turn the lip using pliers and progressing to a hammer and a

Metalworking

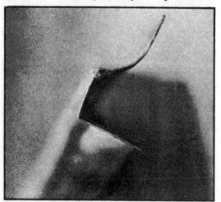

This is the problem area. Rust has formed between the outer and inner wing. About four inches above the wheel arch you can see a moulding line in the wing which is going to offer a stiff area, ideal for resisting welding distortion. As you can see the flared lip on the wheel arch is a complex shape to reproduce.

If we leap ahead to the completed repair section and look at its cross-section it becomes clear that the shape can be divided in two — a right angle section and a concave section. They can be made separately and then welded together.

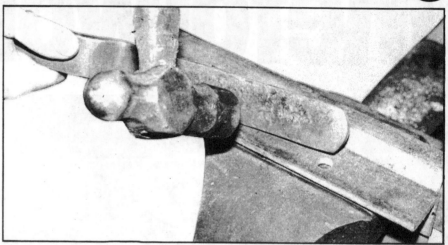

The first stage is to make a right angle section. You can turn a right angle by using two pieces of angle iron in a vice to hold the metal and then turn the angle using a hammer and slapper . . . .

An alternative is to treat yourself to a C.G. Automation bender like this. Scribe the lip dimension on the sheet metal, clamp it in the bender . . . .

. . . . raise the handles until they are horizontal.

The inner, horizontal, lip and the vertical edge should be carefully measured, but at this stage it is the first dimension that is important.

dolly. It is not easy to do neatly and accurately and there is a natural tendency for the beating in the lip to stretch the metal which, in turn, distorts the surface of the panel you are making.

I have developed a habit of making up the flange and panel surface as two components and then welding up the joint. This is not the conventional method and calls for neat edge to edge welding with very little filler rod, but it is fast and works well with practice.

The most common mistake amongst amateur restorers, and I was frequently guilty until I saw somebody make a better job, was to cut out the very minimum of metal to get rid of the rust and then "let-in" a replacement section. It makes much better sense and will produce better results if you cut away and replace a section that coincides with an area of curvature or a moulding line that will impart stiffness in the region of the joint during the welding operation. The other important point to bear in mind is access to both sides of the panel at the point where the joint will occur so that the weld can be dressed (shaped) with a hammer and dolly to reduce the effects of distortion to a minimum.

Now let us turn our attention to wing edge repairs where there is a flared lip. In such cases there are so many curves to take into account that, at first sight, the home-restorer has no chance of making replacement sections. The solution I would suggest is to make a close study of the cross-section and see whether it cannot be made up in stages and welded together.

To show what can be done, I made up a part of the wing edge ready to weld into the Alfa. In principle it is very straight-forward but in practice it is advisable to be patient and prepared to throw away quite a lot of sheet metal before you get it right — even after seven years working sheet metal for a living in the restoration trade, I still describe myself as a beginner, so do not expect to master the skills overnight!

Metal

I prefer working with new sheet metal rather than with bits cut from scrap vehicles if I am making a body part from scratch, rather than adapting an existing panel. The main reasons for this preference are that old paint makes accurate scribing difficult and it can lead to

. . . . and what emerges is a perfect right angle.

The right-angle strip being "tried up" prior to forming the wheel arch profile.

poor welds, and that, in many cases the recovered metal is too thin. For bodywork I usually use 18 SWG (0.048 ins or 1.219mm thick) or 20 SWG (0.030 ins or 0.914mm thick) sheet (never galvanised because you get very poor welds accompanied by dangerous fumes) — anything much thinner has not got enough meat in it. Regular readers will know that I do not recommend screwing or rivetting on patches and I am very strongly against fastening aluminium patches onto steel bodywork and covering them over with filler.

What will form the outer, vertical face is stretched by beating it with the flat pein of the panel hammer. This stretches the metal and should be done in stages, dressing out the hammer marks . . . .

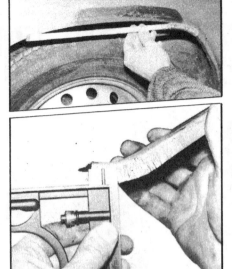

. . . and then trying the result up against the car at regular intervals — if you go too far and introduce too much curvature, start again with a new piece of metal. When you get the curve correct, trim the flange to the right dimension — it grows during the operation.

The next stage is to tackle the concave curve which forms the "flare". In the absence of a rolling machine I took a fairly large piece of sheet metal and pulled it round the shaft of a handy spade which happened to have a suitable radius!

As you can see, the radius was fine but in order to curve the section around the wheelarch I had to narrow the sheet metal section. I then beat the outer edge of the curve until it had both the correct section and curve. It takes a great deal of patience and you must be prepared for some false starts. You have to end up with the outer edge of the curved section matching the lip section you make separately, and the inner surface running in line with the wing.

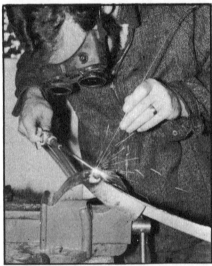

When the two sections match the wing edge, weld them together.

The next stage is to cut the rotten section of the wing away, repair the inner wheel arch edge and then weld in the new section. I would recommend welding an extension onto the repair section you see here, so that it will extend to the body moulding line. In the interests of safety it is a good idea to remove the fuel tank before starting cutting or welding on the car itself. □

METAL CUTTING

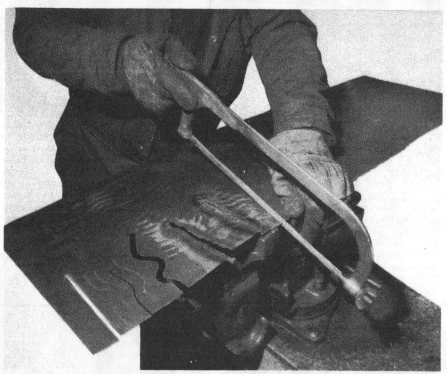

By the Editor

Once you get really involved in maintaining or restoring an old car it won't be long before you become involved in metal cutting and as with most jobs there are several ways to go about it. We shall be taking a look at a selection of methods and suggesting what sort of job each might be used for, but you should not takes those suggestions as hard and fast rules — a lot depends upon w hat equipment you can lay your hands on and upon the nature of the job you are tackling.

HACKSAW

The trusty hacksaw has been around for a long time and is an essential part of the classic car owner's tool kit. It will accurately cut just about any metal with very little wastage or risk of distortion in skilled hands. Disadvantages include a restricted depth of cut between the blade and the saw frame, a lack of manouvreability which makes cutting along a curve difficult and problems when attempting to cut in a restricted space. The saw can only be used where you can get room either side of the cut. It is worthwhile buying a good hacksaw rather than making do with somebody's neglected cast off. I personally heartily dislike using a hacksaw with a horizontal handle — it·is much easier to cut accurately with a handle which is vertical or angled.

It is surprising to see how many people treat a hacksaw blade as a friend for life and struggle manfully with worn out and chipped blades which make cutting very hard work. Long sweeps with the saw rather than "hacking" produce a more accurate result and take less out of you and the blade.

JUNIOR HACKSAW

A smaller version of the hacksaw, this can be used in smaller spaces, but otherwise shares all the characteristics of its big brother.

PAD SAW

Much of what I have said about the hack saw applies to the pad-saw, but it is more manoevrable, needs less working space, can perform any length of cut and is suitable for working blind i.e. where only one surface of the metal being cut is accessible. A useful tool.

HAMMER AND CHISEL

You can cut almost any metal with nothing more sophisticated than a hammer and a chisel, but I certainly would not recommend it for cast items or where anything other than a fairly rough result is acceptable. Even in skilled hands a hammer and chisel is not a particularly accurate method of cutting, although the degree of accuracy does depend a lot upon choosing the right chisel for the job.

For cutting sheet metal I generally prefer to use a bolster or spade chisel with a wide blade, but even with practice accuracy and freedom from distortion are questionable. It is a good idea to wear gloves to protect your hands and wrists from injury and you should not work with a chisel with a burred or mushroomed striking face because if the chisel slips through your fingers it can hurt your hand badly. There is a temptation to use the biggest hammer you can find to drive the chisel, but there will be less chance of missed blows and very tired wrists if you select a hammer of 1½-2 lbs. I was taught not to take my eyes off the cutting edge of the chisel and to ignore the hammer striking the chisel, and every time I have broken this rule I have hurt myself.

AIR CHISEL

I feel that the air chisel is not the ideal tool for the home restorer. Obviously it cannot be used without a fairly large output compressor which is not something many of us have access to and another disadvantage is its destructive nature. An air chisel will cut any sort of sheet steel you are likely to encounter on a motor car but it requires skill to cut sheet metal with accuracy and if the car you are working on is well-rusted the impact of the chisel could do more damage than good, tearing away the evidence of where the things went and making life difficult.

I would strongly recommend wearing thick leather gauntlets when using an air-chisel because it leaves very rough edges and if the chisel does slip you can suffer a very nasty cut.

FLAME CUTTING

For most home restorers flame cutting is not a practical option. Basically, the equipment is expensive and the flame raises the question of fire risk and distortion of sheet metal, metal wastage and lack of accuracy. If you have a gas welding plant you can, of course, borrow or buy a cutting attachment or using the welding torch establish a weld pool and feed an excess of oxygen into the flame whereupon it will cut — I do not like cutting with flame because I think it causes many more problems than it solves, but some people do it all the time. If you do adopt the method leave yourself room for error and take care with the molten metal.

CUTTING DISC

An abrasive cutting disc can only be used with an angle grinder whether it be driven by electricity or air. The disc rotates at between 10,000 and 12,000 r.p.m. and it is important

to use the correct type of disc for the job you are tackling — a masonry cutting disc is different to one intended for cutting steel or cast iron. You should **not** use any rotary cutting tool unless the correct safety guards are in place on the machine, and you must wear protective clear goggles, a face mask, and leather gauntlets which will protect the hands and wrists are desirable. When in use the disc will produce sparks of red hot metal and thick cotton overalls buttoned at the wrists and neck are preferable to working in a T-shirt or open-necked shirt.

If during cutting operations the disc is chipped, discard it and fit a new one for safety's sake. Do not use a damp cutting disc and replace a disc when it is half-worn. Always use the edge of the disc for cutting not the side and do not use a disc intended for cutting to grind down surfaces — there are discs intended for grinding designed to withstand side loads. Ignore these warnings and the disc may break up with highly dangerous results.

The wastage with a cutting disc is very slighty wider than the thickness of the disc and in the hands of a skilled operator considerable accuracy is possible. Manouvreability is good if there is working space for the angle grinder.

Air grinders require quite a large compressor output and you really benefit from having a sizeable reservoir in-line to cope with on-off usage. The major advantage of air cutters is their stall performance — if the disc does jam you can release the trigger to stop the air supply and the tool can be withdrawn without damage to it or danger to the operator.

Electric grinders are probably much more practical for the home-restorer. Talking in general terms there are two sizes to choose from — those that will take four inch grinding or cutting discs and the much more bulky and heavy machines that will take 7 inch discs.

The smaller machine is much more convenient to use, but their small size means that they are often severely over-loaded because the operator expects too much of them have seen sensibly used small angle grinders barely last six months in everyday use in the hands of professionals.

It is very difficult to be specific about the limits of electric grinders, but if you take your time, keep the revs up, and give the machine regular breaks to allow it to cool down, the little machine will tackle most of the cutting jobs required for restoraion.

Hesitance when using the cutting discs is as dangerous as carelessness. You must hold the machine firmly with both hands and keep a finger poised to switch off instantly if the disc jams. Un-plug the angle grinder when it is not in use in case it is accidentally switched on. If it is accidentally switched on take the plug out rather than go near the grinder.

NIBBLER

A nibbler is difficult to describe — if you have studied a sewing machine it is a similar arrangement but with a cutting head in place of the needle. Once you can steer accurately the nibbler is very efficient at cutting sheet metal, but you must have clearance below the

surface of the metal, which restricts the nibbler's use on the body shell.

JIG SAW

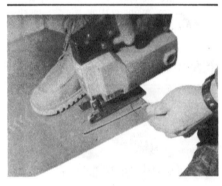

While the nibbler is best employed off the car rather than on panels the jig saw is difficult to use on sheet metal and comes into its own when used to cut panels with the minimum of wastage and distortion. A normal jig saw fitted with a steel cutting blade will cut most gauges of steel used in classic car bodies, however, there are snags. Metal cutting blades are brittle and will break if twisted or allowed to bottom as often happens when cutting in areas where the body is double skinned.

In awkward spots the cost of replacing blades can soon mount up and you may care to

METAL CUTTING

(Continued)

try using half a junior hacksaw blade in the jig saw. They are slightly more forgiving and cost a lot less.

To start cutting it is often necessary to drill a hole wide enough to insert the blade. Steering the jig saw is rather tricky and it pays to cut at a steady pace taking particular care when cutting a radius — always leave a margin for error while you get the hang of this method of cutting.

GOSCUT

This is a manually operated tool and cuts with very little distortion although there is some wastage. It is not usable in some locations and does require the operator to have very strong wrists if any major cutting work is tackled, anything much thicker than 20 gauge sheet steel is going to be hard work.

TIN SNIPS OR SHEARS

Despite their name a large pair of tin snips can cut sheet metal up to 18 gauge — rather more substantial than tin! There is a wide range of tin snips to choose from and two or three different pairs will make a useful addition to any home restorer's tool box. I find that I prefer shears with long handles to give plenty of leverage and bulbous blades, and I have both left and right hand cut shears to suit different jobs.

It is worth buying the best tin snips or shears you can get and taking good care of them — avoid attempting to cut wire or cutting through welds to preserve the edges of the blades and keep both the blades and the pivot pin between them well lubricated.

With practice is it possible to cut very accurately in straight lines or around curves but the metal either side of the cut will have to

move and you must expect some distortion especially where you are cutting a panel — distortion is less of a problem if you are working on sheet metal.

GUILLOTINES

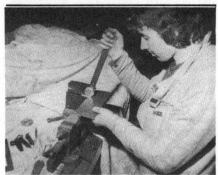

Large guillotines are a god-send to the professional restorer and quite beyond the pocket of the enthusiast — they only cut straight lines, and can only be used on sheet metal, but they do it quickly and accurately. Smaller bench or vice mounted guillotines are available at much less cost and may prove a more versatile option, but, again, they are for sheet metal up to 18 gauge and not suitable for lopping panels off a car.

ACCURACY

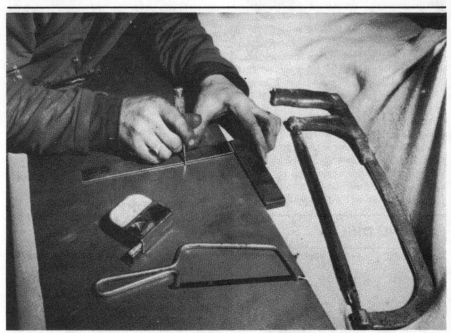

Cutting by eye is not good enough. Time spent measuring and accurately scribing the metal to be cut is vital to the success of any cutting operation. In some cases it may be enough to use a guideline drawn with a felt tip pen, but do make sure that when you are cutting away part of a panel that you leave a shape which is not going to be very difficult to match or weld when you come to position the new metal.

Accurate cutting makes any sort of sheet steel work much easier to do, but allow yourself a margin of error with any cutting

Safety

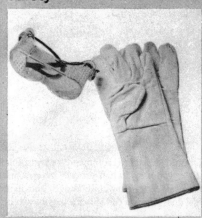

Any metal cutting operation must be approached with a proper regard for safety. Flame or rotary cutting methods call for proper eye protection and gloves — thick leather gauntlets — should provide some degree of protection for the hands and wrists against flying metal particles and edges which can be as sharp as a surgeon's scalpel. The best policy is to over-protect yourself and any bystanders or helpers rather than wonder why you did not on the way to hospital.

tool until you have plenty of experience. Never cut away load bearing metal without first supporting or bracing the structure to compensate for what you will be removing.

When making any repair section on sheet steel cut a larger piece than you will require to allow for errors and the metal taken up in angles — remember that you can trim down to size relatively easily but if you start with too little metal you may have to make the section a second time.

Our thanks to Gable Arc Welding for the loan of power tools used to illustrate this article.

How To Use Your Angle Grinder

by Michael Brisby

Above:
It is particularly effective when used to remove a panel located by a turned over lip, by reducing the edge.

U sed properly the angle grinder is a wonderful tool which will quickly prove indispensible to the person tackling either minor repairs or major restorations.

Choice of Grinder

Where angle grinders are concerned the biggest heaviest industrial quality version is not going to be particularly useful. A 7" grinder has its uses and plenty of power in reserve but it is often difficult to manouvre and far too heavy for prolonged use, particularly when working on your back with the car above you.

A 4½-inches diameter angle grinder is not only much cheaper, but it is both more manouvrable and easier to use in the confined spaces that abound in a car bodyshell. There may be a suspicion that a small grinder is not up to the job, but the small ones I have used lasted six months of practically everyday use in a professional workshop without problems and that represents years of use for the average home restorer who treats the tool sympathetically.

Cutting or grinding processes

There are various types of cutting and grinding discs and flexible backed abrasive discs for use on angle grinders and it is important for both safety and efficiency to select the correct disc and use it for the purpose for which it was designed.

The power supply to the angle grinder must be properly earthed. It is advisable to use an "indestructable" plug, correctly fused, and to check that the cable from the plug to the machine is in good condition. Do not lift the grinder by the cable. Unplug the grinder when it is not in use and particularly when changing discs.

SAFETY

All angle grinders are sold with a partial guard to prevent the worst of the debris being thrown at the operator. Do not use the machine without the guard securely attached as the manufacturer intended, but bear in mind that the guard offers at best, only partial protection. You must wear proper clear eye protection and that cannot be over emphasised. Anyone, spectator or helper within fifteen feet of an angle grinder in use should also wear eye protection. Red hot sparks can embed themselves in glass and paintwork and cannot be removed.

Depending on the make, type and size of the angle grinder at your disposal, the disc will be rotating at 7,500 to 12,000 revolutions per minute so the disc must be mounted on the machine securely (unplug the grinder to do this). It must be in good condition, that is approximately circular and dry — a severe chip can cause the grinder to go out of control and water or oil on the cutting or grinding discs could allow them to break up. Correct usage of flexible discs and grinding discs is at a shallow angle to the work-piece but for some purposes the grinding disc can be used edge on. A cutting disc should only be used edge on, should not be used for grinding and is not designed to cope with side loading.

What you can do

The variety of tasks an angle grinder can perform are many, and it is one of the most-

used tools in a professional body shop. Reducing welds is one typical use, grinding back the metal so that the welded joint between two panels becomes nearly invisible. The grinder is equally effective in 'cleaning up' local areas prior to welding or other repairs, getting rid of rust scale and old paint. Be careful that you don't take too much good metal off, however, causing a deep groove or an over-weak area; nor is an angle grinder the ideal instrument with which to strip paint from a large area — this is best done by hand with paint-stripper.

A cutting disc must be used edge on to the work and should not be subjected to twisting or side loads. The disc on the right is intended for grinding and is best used at a shallow angle to the work. Choose the correct disc for the job in hand.

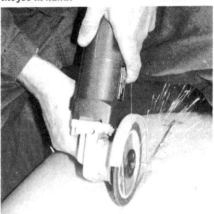

With practice the "wastage" inherent in the cutting process with an angle grinder is only fractionally wider than the cutting disc. There is little or no risk of the cut edges distorting and you only need access to one side of the item being cut. Try not to force the pace with an angle grinder, let the abrasive disc do the work, but do machine firmly. With practice you can cut very accurately and quickly.

The rapidity with which the cutting disc can get through metal makes removing old panels very easy, as you can slice off an old wing in minutes, allowing open access to any mounting bolts after the old panel has dropped away. Seized bolts can also be cut through, and spot welds can be broken by applying the grinder to them (paint strip the metal first to reveal where they are). Panels which over-lap can also be removed by grinding the lip where the metal is folded over a frame, as on a door skin. New metal repair patches can also be cut out with reasonable accuracy. All in all, after the first few hours using one you'll wonder how you ever managed without an angle grinder! □

drilling and tapping

*John Williams
gets you out of trouble
with broken bolts
and stripped threads*

Imagine that whilst removing a cylinder head from your engine one or more of the retaining studs or bolts shears — you have no choice, it has to come out, how do you go about rescuing the situation?

Probably the first thing to do is to remove the cylinder head and place clean rags down the exposed cylinder bores to protect them. With the head off you may find your luck is in and that a very useful length of the broken stud (or studs) is left sticking up above the deck of the cylinder block. The polite way to try and remove the stud is by cutting a slot in the stud and using a screw-driver probably won't work because you cannot apply enough force and penetrating oil; even if you create a plasticine reservoir around the stud and give the oil twelve hours or more to soak in it could still prove a disappointment.

You can, if there is room, use a stud extractor and they really are good — beating pliers of any description hands down — but if they do not give a good grip first time you can have problems and there is the risk that the stud will snap again — probably flush with the block face.

Heat from a blow-lamp or a welding torch can be a great help in undoing stubborn nuts and bolts but there are serious risks if the offending stud or bolt is in a casting because differing rates of expansion (particularly with a steel stud in an aluminium casting) can split the casting. If you have the tackle you can try brazing a nut on to what is left of the stud and once everything has cooled down using a spanner on the nut, but you have to be careful.

If you have tried everything else or if the stud has broken off almost flush with the face of the casting you still have one more "short-cut" and that is to use an "Easy-Out". This is

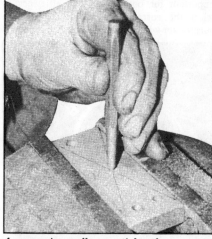

Accuracy is usually essential to the success of a job involving drilling and tapping. The work should be carefully marked where possible by scribing lines which intersect where drilling is needed; the position for drilling can then be clearly marked with a centre punch.

a tool with a tapered left-hand thread (for removing studs etc with right-hand threads) which is available in various sizes and is used in conjunction with a spanner or tap wrench. The "Easy-Out" is screwed anti-clockwise into a hole drilled centrally through the stud and the theory is that a point will be reached at which the extractor will penetrate the stud no further and the stud itself will turn. This method is not always successful, partly because there is a tendency for the extractor to expand the stud as it penetrates thus locking the stud even more firmly within the block.

More often than not the only reliable method of removing a broken stud is to drill it out and to tap a new thread for a new stud. The early stages of this job are the same as for using an "Easy-Out". The first job is to cut or file the stud level with the face of the block. This is important and helps to ensure that the drilling which follows will be accurate and that the "Easy-Out" (if used) will penetrate the stud from the outset and not merely 'spread' the protruding part of the stud,

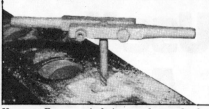

Here an Easy-out is being used on a broken stud which has been filed level with the block and drilled centrally as described in the text.

bearing in mind that if the "Easy-Out" is unsuccessfull further accurate drilling will be needed. The next job is to centre punch the stud accurately not only marking the centre of the stud but providing the starting point for the first drill. The first hole should be drilled with the smallest available drill (1/16" is recommended but 1/8" will do) and great care should be taken to ensure that the hole passes through the **centre** of the stud until the drill emerges at the other end. Accuracy is all important, and the minimum force should be used so as to keep the drill parallel with the stud.

When drilling great care should be taken to ensure that the drill is kept square to the work. A beginner would find it worthwhile to have an assistant keeping a check on this for him. The drill should not be forced as this could distort the hole and even break a bit.

Taps and dies are usually sold in boxed sets covering a range of sizes. Whereas taps are normally used in sets of three, dies (not shown here) are usually adjustable, are used to cut the thread on a metal rod, and only one die is needed for a given size of thread.

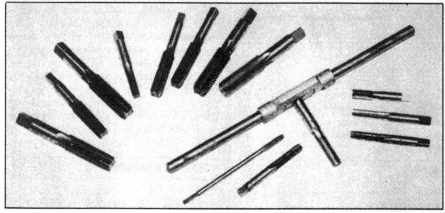

The hole is then enlarged using a drill not larger than about half the diameter of the stud. To some extent the second drill will follow the existing hole, but again care should be taken to keep the drill parallel with the stud. Now the "Easy-Out" can be tried but if it fails the next stage is to drill once more. The drill which is used this time should be checked in an identical stud hole to ensure that it fits closely without damaging the threads, and the purpose of this drilling is to remove the remains of the seized stud leaving its thread as well as the thread in the casting intact. Having done this it is sometimes possible to separate the remaining thread near the top of the stud hole using a very fine punch or chisel and then extract the thread using a small screwdriver or pointed pliers. If you are successful the thread in the block can be cleaned using a tap of the correct size and it will be ready to accept a new stud. If the thread in the block becomes damaged it will be necessary to drill it out completely and cut a new thread, and this will require a slightly thicker stud.

The tap should be inserted and kept parallel to the hole, lubricated as necessary and never forced.

Taps are for cutting internal threads and are generally bought in sets which include a selection of dies which are used to cut external threads. Both taps and dies are a useful addition to the restorer's tool kit not only because they can be used to "recover" threads on components which might otherwise be useless but also because they can allow you to go a size up (tapped internal threads) or a size down (external threads cut with a die) to get round the problem of damaged or severely worn threads.

In general, taps are intended to be used in sets of three. The diameter of the new stud or bolt and the size of the thread to be cut will determine the correct set of taps to be used and the most suitable drill size for those taps. Various booklets are available containing tables of these dimensions for easy reference. The first tap to be used, known as the "taper" tap is designed to cut a shallow thread with about two thirds of its cutting section; the remaining third cuts the full size thread. When cutting a thread in a thin sheet of metal the second and third taps may not be needed. The second or intermediate tap cuts a full size

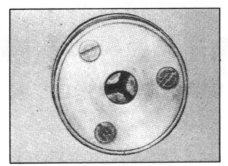

When the broken stud is accessible a stud extractor is often effective. These usually work by means of serrated cams which grip the stud as the extractor is being turned.

There are various types of stud extractor and they are used in conjunction with a spanner or a half inch square drive as used for sockets.

thread along two thirds of its cutting section and the bottoming or plug tap along its entire cutting section.

The blunt end of a tap is formed into a square section to fit a tap wrench which may have a chuck (similar to a drill) or be adjustable. Having carefully drilled a hole of the appropriate size for the tap it is still essential that the tap is kept parallel to the hole when in use to produce threads of even thickness all around the hole and to the required depth. No force should be needed when turning the tap in the hole, and it is advisable to turn the tap anti-clockwise a quarter of a turn at frequent intervals to help clear the swarf produced. The swarf is accommodated in three fluted areas between the cutting edges of a tap and if there is any tendency for the tap to become jammed in the hole no force should be used but the tap should be unscrewed from the hole and cleaned before the job is continued. Plenty of light oil should be used to lubricate a tap when working in steel, paraffin should be used when working in aluminium, and no lubricant is required when tapping in brass or cast iron. Blind holes (those which do not go right through the metal) need to be deeper than the required thread to accommodate the point of the tap.

A tap which becomes stuck is very easily broken, often leaving the broken part entirely within the hole. Avoid this by keeping the tap parallel to the hole, lubricating well (where appropriate) and avoiding force when the tap

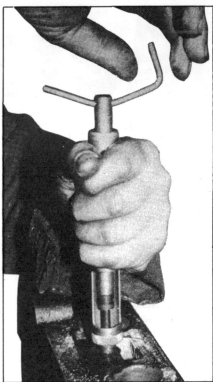

Although not available outside the trade Helicoils offer an alternative to tapping and are frequently used to replace the threads in sparking plug holes. A Helicoil is similar to a coil spring with one end turned across the diameter forming a tab which fits the slot in the special tool shown here . . .

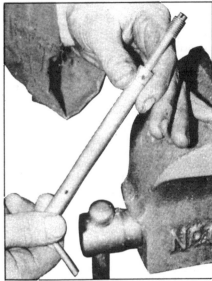

. . . Once screwed into place the handle of the special tool is turned back slightly breaking the tab.

appears to be binding in the hole. In soft metals such as brass the tap may feel as if it is cutting smoothly but an accumulation of swarf can damage the new threads as they are being cut. Avoid this by removing the tap from the hole carefully from time to time and cleaning it. Take care to avoid breaking a tap by forcing it against the bottom of a blind hole. □

The writer would like to thank DAK Autos and Dorel Engines Ltd (both at Luton) for their assistance in the preparation of this article.

Metalworking

Part 1

In this new series of articles we will be covering all aspects of metalworking for the do-it-yourself restorer starting this month with a guide to buying, cutting and folding metal. Future articles will cover panel beating techniques, then brazing, welding etc.

Buying sheet metal

The first problem for the do-it-yourself restorer is to find a local supplier of sheet metal. The 'Yellow Pages' or other local trades directory might help; try looking under 'Iron and steel Stockists', 'Steel stockholders' etc. Alternatively, ask your local professional repairer or restorer where he gets his supplies – he may even sell you some from his own stock.

We are assuming of course that you are having to make your own repair sections or complete panels because they are not available 'off the shelf'. Before shopping for metal you will need to know the thickness required, and, if you have a clean sample of the metal used in the original panel (free of paint, underseal, etc) you can measure this with a micrometer, Vernier caliper, or a Standard Wire Gauge. The thickness of metal is described as a certain 'gauge', this being an abbreviation of Standard Wire Gauge. Body panels are often 20 or 22 gauge, chassis box sections 16 or 14 gauge or thicker. The lower the figure the thicker the metal.

Although a steel stockholder is likely to have everything that you will need, some insist upon a minimum order which will be far in excess of your requirements. On the other hand, many motor factors and panel shops stock a limited amount of sheet steel and tend to sell it in 3' x 2' or 4' x 2' sizes, whereas stockholders sizes will be 6' x 3' or 8' x 4', the larger sheets providing better value for money.

When buying sheet steel it might well be worth the slightly larger expense of investing in Zintec. This is a mild steel with a protective zinc coating which has a better resistance to rust than plain mild steel and it is particularly recommended for chassis members, outriggers and floor panels. Zintec *does* lend itself to gas and MIG welding and should not be confused with galvanised steel. Galvanised steel should not be welded because it gives off harmful zinc oxide fumes.

So far we have been dealing with sheet steel, but aluminium is available in the same sizes and thicknesses.

Steve Demol is making a repair panel for our Land-Rover's bulkhead, folding the sheet steel by clamping it between lengths of timber along the line of the fold and using a leather mallet. A good solid engineers vice firmly mounted on a strong bench is invaluable for all types of metalwork.

Cutting sheet metal

The methods which you choose for cutting your sheet metal will depend upon what equipment you can afford and also upon the sizes and thicknesses of the pieces to be cut and the complexity of their shapes. Taking a broader view, what you can or should afford may also depend upon the amount of restoration work to be undertaken, and the cost of other equipment which is also needed for panel beating, welding etc. Obviously you may be able to justify a larger outlay on more sophisticated equipment if you are planning a succession of restoration projects. On the other hand, if you have only one project in mind it is hardly worth putting money into expensive equipment just to make the job a little easier or to save time, and especially if such an outlay will leave you short of funds for vital equipment or parts later on.

A good pair of snips would be a worthwhile investment – say a pair of 12"-14" straight or handed snips for which you may expect to pay £15-18. Don't buy the cheapest available. Snips should be able to cut 20 gauge steel and thinner (and 16 or even 14 gauge aluminium). Thicker metal can be cut with a hacksaw, and having acquired these two basic tools (and don't forget the simple hammer and chisel or

---

Buying, cutting and folding sheet metal, by John Williams.

The basic cutting tools are a hacksaw for thicker metals, and snips for thin sheet. Although snips come in various sizes, one good pair should serve most purposes but don't buy cheap ones – like cheap scissors they blunt more quickly and the blades tend to separate under load.

You can also use a hammer and a sharp chisel to cut sheet metal. Here a hole is being cut and the edges will be tidied with a file afterwards.

The Monodex cutter is an interesting type of cutter which actually removes a strip of metal about ⅛" wide along the cut – thus there is no distortion and it can be used (having drilled a hole from which to start cutting) for cutting panels off cars, even around curved panels. Using a Monodex cutter does require quite a lot of physical effort though.

Small metal folders are designed to be held in the vice. The sheet metal is clamped in place by the top plate (which is removable) and the folding blade is operated by the two hand levers.

The following table shows the Standard Wire Gauge (SWG) size against the actual thickness of sheet metal.	
22 SWG = 0.028"	16 SWG = 0.064"
20 SWG = 0.036"	14 SWG = 0.080"
18 SWG = 0.048"	12 SWG = 0.104"

We find our rotary shear cutter a very useful tool which, firmly bolted to the bench, will slice though 18 gauge steel with an easy lever action – AND it will cut gentle curves as well as straight lines.

bolster) you then have an almost bewildering choice of other cutting equipment. For example, we find a rotary shear useful in our Beckenham workshop. Ours is a Metcut (as advertised in *Practical Classics* at £30.99 incl VAT) which is bolted to the bench for ease of operation, and it will make straight cuts or follow gentle curves, coping easily with steel up to 18 gauge. The Nibblex is an effective cutting tool for up to 18 gauge steel or 16 gauge aluminium. It is a power drill attachment which is equally useful for cutting new sheet metal or for removing panels from the car. The cutting part of the Nibblex is a small punch which becomes worn in time but which can be replaced quite cheaply. At the time of writing the Nibblex is being advertised at £14.65 inclusive, and £1.55 each for the replacement punches.

If you already have a jig saw then that too can be used for cutting metal but you must use the correct blades. Power hacksaws, usually air driven, are also available and an air or electrically driven angle grinder is useful because it will cut metal and can also be used later to tidy up your welds.

Special nozzles are available for the better gas welding equipment which will enable you to make clean fine cuts in metal. Arc welding equipment can be used for cutting using special cutting rods, but this method should be applied with discretion as heat distortion is a problem, and it will not cut cleanly.

Folding sheet metal

The equipment needed for folding sheet metal will depend on the complexity of the work to be done but there is plenty of scope for improvisation. Top hat sections and box sections and other repair panels which incorporate several

CONTINUED ON PAGE 36

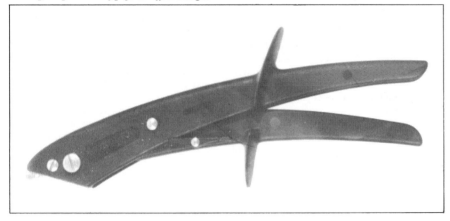

Metalworking

Part 2

I have always imagined that an experienced panel beater is one of those enviable people who make a highly skilled task look very easy, and this has been confirmed for me over recent weeks by Steve Demol, our resident 'body man'.

The targets we set ourselves for this second episode in the Metalworking Series were as follows; to outline the basic set of tools which would be required by the DIY panel beater and to explain a little about their uses; to follow a simple dent removal procedure and to illustrate the making of a reasonably basic repair panels. This information, together with a little theory and some helpful hints, should provide a grounding of useful knowledge for even the complete beginner.

The Tools

There is a vast and confusing selection of tools available for panel beating, though a great many of them have a specialised function that need not concern us here since they involve highly advanced techniques. For the beginner the tools which are chosen will largely depend upon the amount of money you have to spend. Unfortunately, the tools at the cheaper end of the market are not of a very high quality and so if at all possible, avoid purchasing these. The most important factor affecting a hammer or dolly (the panel beaters two basic tools) is its hardness, and this obviously depends on the metal that it is made from. The cheaper tools are made from mild steel which is a lot softer than the high carbon steel used for the more expensive products. It is vitally important that the shiny surfaces of both hammers and dollies remain clean and smooth and this is where the cheap tools fall down. Their softer construction allows them to quickly become pitted forming patterns on their surfaces, which can then be transferred to the panel under repair.

The kit of tools that we chose as being a suitable starting point for the DIY user contains three sorts of hammer and a pair of general purpose dollies. The two ball pein hammers are included since they are ideal for general light work. Everyone should have one as they are especially suitable when using centre punches and drifts. Different weights simply determine the use of the hammer. The hide mallet is good for panels with heavy denting as it can be used with a fair degree of abandon

without risk of bruising the metal. This 'protection' is provided by the replaceable hide inserts that form the hitting faces, and as these mallets can be found weighing up to 2½ lbs, they are a very useful tool. The second type of hammer shown is the panel beater or planishing hammer, and this is designed specifically for working the metal. They should on no account be used with punches or chisels as the smoothness of their faces is the main factor affecting their usefulness. The two dollies illustrated here are both cast from stainless steel, but the more common varieties are made from mild steel (cheaper ones) or high carbon steel (more expensive and harder).

The function of the dolly is to provide the solid base onto which the panel can be shaped. These general purpose dollies are made to include many of the common curvatures which will be needed in 99% of work-shop situations, although there are many other more specialised versions available.

The basic principles

It's all very well kitting yourself out with a good selection of high quality tools, but without a smattering of basic information related to the task, results may be hard to achieve. Panel beating is definitely an activity where it is all in the wrist action, and putting this into practice is half the art. The hammers should be held towards the end of the shaft and never gripped tightly. The tool has virtually to be flicked by the fingers and thumb, assisted by flexing the wrist, to provide the hammering action. Just being able to do this takes practice and once it has been mastered, the strength and uniformity of the blows should be examined. In panel beating an ability to start a 'course' across a panel and maintain it for the whole run is a valuable and indeed, an

Chris Graham investigates the 'gentle' art of panel beating

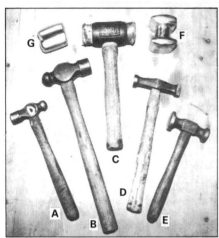

A suitable selection for a beginner; A — Ball Pein ¾lb hammer, B — Ball Pein 2lb hammer, C — Hide mallet, D/E — Planishing hammers (square and round faces), F/G — general purpose dollies.

essential asset.

By the very nature of the subject, panel beating involves the distortion (or further distortion when repairing accident damage) of the original metal. Both shrinking and stretching occurs and these two functions lead to the metal becoming work hardened and so more rigid. A panel which has been badly damaged in an accident absorbs the shock of the impact over a wide area, and this results in a series of channels and ridges being formed. The distorted areas furthest from the impact point represent the indirect damage, and in these the metal has not usually been bent beyond its elastic limit and so is not permanently damaged. The direct damage areas however are usually more seriously distorted and have become hardened into that position. As a general rule accident damage should be tackled in reverse order to the way it was caused, thus the indirect damage is corrected first, followed by the more serious direct damage.

It appears that there is no hard and fast method to be applied when removing a dent from a panel. All distortions have their own particular characteristics and so have to be treated in an individual way as the situation demands. However, the two most commonly

Planishing hammers with only a slightly curved face are most suitable for the DIY user. Make sure the faces of both hammers and dollies are clean and polished at all times.

used techniques for simple dent correction involve either 'on' or 'off' the dolly methods. On the dolly or 'direct' beating is a particularly useful technique when it comes to dealing with convex distortions and ridges. A dolly should be selected whose face matches as closely as possible the original contour of the panel. This face is then held directly beneath the damaged area, and light blows with a beating hammer (of suitable weight) building to a heavier action, are used to shrink the metal back into place. It is important to take things gently and not to flatten the defect in one heavy blow, and when dealing with a ridge move along its length in a methodical manner to lower it as a whole.

The hammer of your choice should be gripped only lightly and near the base of its shaft.

Off the dolly or 'indirect' beating provides the ideal technique for raising depressions in panels. Again a suitable dolly is selected and held directly beneath the depression, but this time the beating hammer blows are directed at the depressions' associated ridges around its edge. This gives the effect of a two blow action, one as the hammer hits, and the second as the dolly reacts and is forced upwards. Once the major part of the depression has been corrected, the direct method can be reverted to for the final finishing or planishing.

Sizeable dents require a little more force to get things moving, and so a hide or pear shaped mallet (this is exactly as it sounds) are the ideal tools for this. In most cases this type of dent is too large for a hand held dolly to be used, and a much larger area is required as a base.

The real test of a panel beater's skill is his ability to fabricate repair sections and panels from flat sheets of metal. This was the task that we set Steve as the last part of this investigation. The results that he achieved and how he achieved them can be assessed from the photographs and captions which followed his procedure. The repair panel which we decided to make was for the front bottom edge of a Gazelle wing. This is a double curvature panel that is typical of many on the older classics.

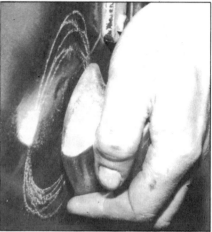

A sure grip on the dolly is essential. One slip here could cost you an hour correcting a mis-aimed blow.

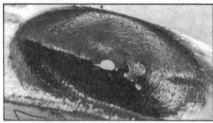

A typical dent like this can, with sufficient practise, be completely repaired.

Large dents are best tackled initially with a moderately heavy hammer against a suitably large base. When working on a large surface like this wooden sheet, remember to keep the panel moving in relation to your hitting. If you fail to do this, flat spots and even stretching may be the unfortunate result.

With the worst of the dent removed turn the panel over, and using the hide mallet and a suitable dolly, roughly work in the original curvature as best you can.

A planishing hammer, a dolly and patience are the ingredients needed to finish the repair.

Now to make our wing repair section: A home made sand-bag (an old leather apron and some boot laces) filled with fine silver sand would provide the base on which the repair panel could be moulded.

With measurements having been taken from the original (carefully allowing for the curvatures), a slightly oversized piece of sheet was cut and the initial blows were struck with the hide mallet directly onto the sand bag.

Progress can be quite rapid at this stage so be careful not to get carried away. Obviously making the first bend on a square sheet requires a good deal of understanding about the angles needed for the finished panel. The left hand is used to apply a gentle pressure to enhance the hammer action.

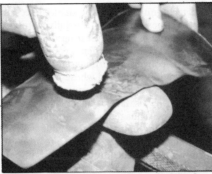

As the bending progresses creases called 'puckers' develop which have to be made good before they grow too large. In this example we used a tool called a Stake, (which is like a dolly with a shaft attached allowing it to be clamped in the vice), as a base onto which we beat out the puckers.

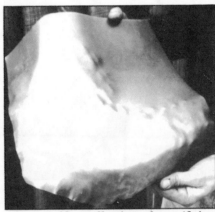

After several hours of beating and many 'fittings' over the original for comparison, we had reached this stage. The shape was roughly there although the area in the centre still required some further stretching to form the bulge present in the original. This was a tricky process as any attempt at stretching the middle resulted in a distortion at either end. The longer we went on however, the more work hardened the metal became which made it less inclined to flex. This made the moulding process a little more predictable and so easier.

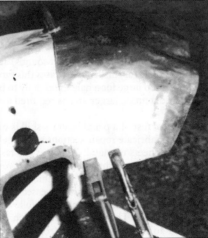

With the awkward bulge in place and the rest of the panel in line, it was clamped to the rest of the wing for a final fitting.

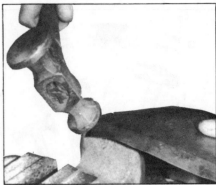

A slight lip was required to match in with the rest of the wheel arch and this was done simply over the edge of the stake with a planishing hammer. This is an operation that requires a 'good eye', and Steve made it look very easy.

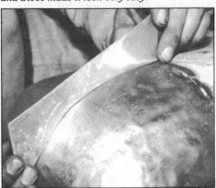

Before we cut away the old metal from the wing we made a set of patterns to exactly record the original curvatures across the panel. Then once the new panel had been tack welded into place these could be used to check for any final adjustments that needed to be made.

The final smooth finish was only achieved after a great deal more planishing and the use of some emery paper to highlight any high spots, which were then individually hammered out.

To sum up it must be said that panel beating is not a skill that you can pick up after a few hours hammering; patience is quite definitely one of the panel beater's most important virtues. Just making this one small panel took Steve several hours although little time was wasted. □

NEXT MONTH
A further look at the basic techniques of panel beating.

Metalworking

Part 3

In last month's 'Metalworking' feature I dealt in a general way with the major aspects of fabricating a repair panel. As it turned out, the panel which we made demanded the application of some fairly advanced beating techniques, which we felt the beginner might find hard to match. So in this month's article we aim to examine more closely, the 'fundamentals' involved.

Bending sheet steel to form an angle or introducing a single curvature is relatively simple – you are only working the metal in a single plane. Once you start to create a section which curves in two planes – a compound curve — life becomes much more difficult.

Although it may take some doing it helps if you can visualise the sheet of metal you are going to create the compound curve in as a square of plasticine or pastry which can be squeezed and stretched between your fingers to form a shape – the only difference is that with metal you have to use more force. This can be applied by beating the metal with a mallet or hammer, or by squeezing the sheet between two rollers on a wheeling machine – a piece of equipment you will not find in many home workshops.

The metal will not easily assume the shape you want; panel beating is about the controlled distortion of the sheet metal to the required contour. It is far easier to stretch or expand a section of sheet metal than it is to shrink it or contract it so your aim must be to create shapes by taking advantage of the differential between areas you have beaten and those you have not, or those you have beaten extensively and those you have beaten lightly. So the emphasis is strongly upon controlled beating.

I did not mention that force has to be applied to achieve the required distortion but all you will create if you resort to a few wild blows with the heaviest hammer you can lift striking against the most solid backing you can find will be scrap metal – innumerable relatively light blows in the right area and administered progressively is the route to success. Even this will not produce the required results if the hammer blows are haphazard – the hammer face should hit the metal surface flat and each blow should overlap the last. Forget swinging the hammer like a blacksmith – a wrist movement is what is

required and, yes, until you are used to it this is very hard on the wrist!

It is perhaps wise first to study a little about the actual structure of metal, and how this relates to the way it behaves when stressed. To obtain satisfactory results 'under the hammer', a metal must have the correct properties. It must be both malleable (easily shaped by hammering when cold, without fracturing), and ductile (resistant to cracking under stress), and it should have an appreciable tensile strength (resistance to fracturing when under tension).

The physical process of hammering an area of metal has, not surprisingly, a considerable effect on its structure. All metals feature a crystaline structure, and it is this property which leads to the characteristic hardness and rigidity, but also allows it to be deformed. In order to re-shape a piece of metal the crystal structure has to be forcibly altered, and this is allowed to occur along what are known as slip planes. These are in effect, the dividing lines between individual crystals, which enables them to slide over one another once a stress is applied.

Chris Graham looks into more secrets of beating metal.

Metalworking Part 3

1

The first task was to run a course of beating straight down an untouched sample of steel sheet, or 'blank' as it is more commonly known. We were hitting onto the sand bag using a hide mallet as this is heavier than the equivalently sized pear shaped example. The lefthand is used to steady the sheet, but at the same time, to apply gentle pressure in the desired direction. It is important to move the metal and not the hammer as this helps to ensure continuity in both the weight of the blows and the effect that they produce.

2

This basic technique produces a curve in the sheet that can easily be regulated to any degree. The advantage is that the base remains flat – with practice of course.

3

Small curves and lips can most simply be 'set in' over the edge of the bench. Make sure that the area of bench chosen is both clean and even – blemishes are very easily picked up but can prove extremely hard to remove. In this case you move the hammer rather than the job, so the regularity and evenness of the blows is particularly important. Remember also to continue the course right across the panel, do not be tempted to stop half way and go back to repair any mistakes that you have already made.

An induced deformity, as well as altering the crystal arrangement, also changes the shape of the individual crystals, and it is this change which leads to a process called work hardening.

This occurs once the crystals have become sufficiently distorted to become irregular and

4

Removing a single curve from a sheet like this is just a matter of hitting it out onto a flat surface (as we reported last month, dollies are used for accident repairs to damaged panels in situ). Care must be taken however, to avoid using too firm a blow in the early stages as this will just distort the sheet in the other direction. Gradually work the curve out by running down its length with calculated blows. Once again check the surface of the bench — it's no good flattening the sheet onto a half embedded screw head.

5

Double curves and twists are created in a similar fashion using the same hitting technique, the only difference is that the lefthand does a little more work. It has to apply the pressure along the two planes required for the curve, at the same time. This technique demands a lot of practice before it can be confidently attempted 'for real'. Removing such a curve is best done using the sandbag, and as a general rule, tackle the largest curve first.

elongated. This change in shape makes it less easy for them to slip over each other, which in turn restricts the movement available, and thus the metal appears to harden.

These factors obviously limit the amount of 'working' that the metal can endure under normal conditions, before it hardens up and becomes unworkable. However, there is a process called annealing which is a simple heat treatment, that restores the metal to its original softness and allows the work to be continued. In most cases, if the metal is

heated to a dull red heat, then this will be sufficient to return the crystals to their original size – a process known as re-crystalising – and so to their original 'flexibility'. It is possible to combine both the working and the re-crystalising, and shape the metal whilst hot. Care is needed however when softer metals such as aluminiums are being annealed, for the heat levels required in such cases can be quite critical. Aluminium can literally be melted over a gas ring, as it has a melting point of just 660 degrees C. A useful technique that can be used to hopefully avoid such a happening involves smearing the surface with soap. This will turn brown as soon as the correct temperature is reached. Quenching the sample in water (from dull red to black heat) can greatly accelerate the process, but still achieve the desired result. Annealing together with other heat treatments will be covered in greater detail, later in this series.

Moving on to more practical matters, the first consideration must be the condition of the sample you intend to beat. The sheet needs to be closely inspected so that any damaged or scratched areas are located and dealt with. Such deformities need to be removed at this stage as they can lead to unsightly blemishes and even structural weaknesses in the final article. Surface scratches are removed with emery cloth, but there is obviously a limit to what you can correct so if considerable blemishes are evident, think about a replacement sheet.

Once your sample has been checked, the next task is to cut and shape it. The cutting involves a little thought as it is easy to be fooled by the size of the sheet in relation to the size of the object which you intend to make. The curves are obviously the hardest areas to judge in terms of material needed, but a useful way of providing a rough guide to the dimensions needed is as follows. If for the sake of argument, you are intending to construct a U-sectioned channel, then the width of sheet required can be approximately calculated by using the simple method illustrated in the diagram. 'X' represents the half-width of the sheet needed to facilitate a curve of that dimension once the stretching has taken place. If the section shown represented a *bowl*, then 'X' would represent the radius of the circle of sheet metal needed at the start.

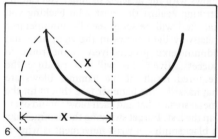

6

Our practical experiments can be followed using the accompanying photographs and their captions.

Having determined the dimensions required and cut out the shape, the edges should be de-burred. This serves several purposes, not the least of them being safety. Aged snips can produce razor sharp edges as well as burrs and neither react favourably with the tightly gripping, ungloved hand. The trusty sandbag can also come a poor second to a ruthless burr, and what's more the burrs can, if beaten, develop into weak areas or even cracks.

The object now was to create a dish from this freshly cut blank. The formation of a dish or bowl is not simply a matter of hitting the plate in the middle until it caves in – there is a degree of method and subtlety involved which takes considerable skill. It is a good idea to first chalk on a rough spiral in the manner shown. This can then act as a guide for your hammering. The idea is to start from the outside edge and work progressively in, but avoiding the actual centre — this area can easily become distorted and can be most difficult to correct.

The disc should be rotated under the hammer and the initial blows should be fairly light. Each blow should ideally be delivered a little in advance of the point of contact with the sandbag. In other words, with the blank held at a slight angle to the bag the edge is the only area making contact, and so a blow delivered a short distance in from this edge, will create the greatest 'stretching' force.

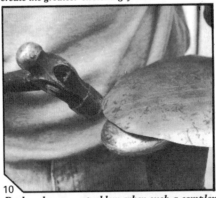

Puckers become a problem when such a complex form is fashioned. These should be dealt with as they occur and are best removed with a conventional hammer on a stake as shown (The stake being tightly gripped in a vice for this). There appears to be no hard and fast method of dispersing them, just ensure that the job is positioned over an area of the stake with the correct curvature, and hit. Often one big pucker will split into two little puckers after such treatment, but do not despair, a couple of blows to each should deal with the problem.

I would like to finish with a few well thought out words of helpful wisdom, but this poses a slight problem. Every technique that Steve Demol demonstrates is done so quickly and made to look so very simple, that one is given the impression that it is all

The work rapidly becomes work hardened and then requires annealing. We stopped short of doing this and were content to planish the piece as it stood. This was done as described last month, on the stake with a planishing hammer.

Re-straightening the dish basically involved reversing the forming procedure. Most of the deformities were corrected on the sandbag, and the final flattening was completed using a flat surface and a piece of wood as shown. Again, hand dollies take the place of the sandbag for accident repairs made on the car.

ridiculously easy. However, the reality of the situation is a little less encouraging. As I tried to stress in last month's feature, the skills of panel beating cannot be picked up in ten minutes. It is very easy to become disillusioned with your first efforts – over enthusiastic hammering is a common fault initially. However, with practice, a growing ability to produce repair sections and panels should provide much satisfaction, as well as being financially worthwhile when the price of the commercially produced article is considered.   □

Metalworking

Part 4

Now that modern welding technology has taken a firm hold in the metalwork shop of today, the old fashioned methods of joining sheet metal, such as riveting, have been forced into second place. However, there still appears to be a most definite niche for these techniques in the specialist markets where the older skills remain firm favourites. This idea, together with the suitability of riveting for the DIY user, has prompted us to concentrate on this area for this month's feature.

Riveting, although an elementary technique, does involve a little more than meets the eye. The chances are that most people who are new to the subject will conjure up images of the hand held Pop riveter and a selection of Pop rivets as being all that riveting entails, but this is not the case. As our title suggests, the involvement of both marking out and drilling can virtually be put on an equal footing with the riveting itself, if a neat and professional job is to be produced.

Marking out is the first important stage in the riveting process, and for obvious reasons, it has to be accurate. The selection of tools required is not very extensive, or even expensive, but they are important. Dividers, set squares, 6 and 12 inch steel rules, a tape measure, a scriber, punches, drills and a hammer are what is required, and with these there should be no excuse for getting it wrong. It is important to be methodical in your actions, never approximate and always work from a set datum point. To illustrate what is required we chose to join two sheets of metal together with a simple straight line of rivets. Always remember, once you have cut your sheet, to de-burr the edges.

Having established the dimensions of the lap joint to be used, a straight line was marked across the upper of the two sheets. This was done using a set square, a steel rule and a pencil. Ensure that the set square is tight against the edge of the sheet, then rest the rule against the square's blade to make sure that it too is square. When marking sheet metal, always draw the marking tool towards the body. This helps avoid the risk of it straying from the rule or slipping on to a painted area nearby. If you are having to join

Pop riveting is probably the simplest and most commonly recognised type of riveting.

two points with a straight line, the sensible way to do it is this. Place the marking tool on the datum point first, and then bring the rule to it, rather than the other way around. If this method is not adopted, considerable errors can arise, especially over long distances.

With the sheet marked the next task is to decide upon the number and spacing of the rivets to be used. This is easy, and simply involves some elementary division once the number of rivets and the length of the row has been established.

Rather than marking out the spacings from a rule, it is a good idea to set the dividers at the desired gap, and then to 'hop' this along the line marking as you go. Once you have completed this, and double checked it for silly mistakes, the marks have to be punched and drilled. When using a punch on a sheet of

metal ensure that you work on a flat, hard and clean surface. A base that is too soft will allow larger than normal indentations to be produced by the punch, and this, over a long distance, can produce a considerable distortion in the panel. Actually punching the metal should only involve one blow from the hammer. If however, several blows are needed check the point of the punch, as it may be blunt. The purpose of using the punch is of course to provide a starting point for the drill.

When drilling, it is best if both sheets are drilled simultaneously. The two should be securely clamped together, and also to the bench if possible, to ensure that there is correct alignment between the holes. Once the row has been drilled, each hole should be de-burred by hand with a large drill. A conve-

Snap, Crackle and Pop — Chris Graham investigates marking out, drilling and riveting.

1
The tools for the job — not terribly expensive, but the right tools in good condition make it so much easier to achieve good results.

2
On zinc coated sheet (as in this example), a pencil produces a more obvious mark than a plain scribe.

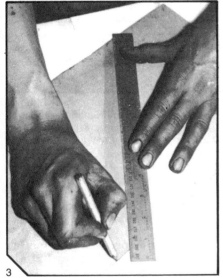

3
Always place the marker on the measured point first, and bring the rule to it. Doing it the other way can lead to inaccuracy.

4
Using a pair of dividers is the most effective and accurate way of marking out a line for holes.

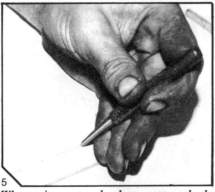

5
When using a punch always approach the marked point from the side — never put the punch straight down on to it from above — it's much harder to judge that way.

6
The automatic punch is a useful tool when working in confined areas. It can be operated by one hand simply by pressing down on the point. The degree of indentation is regulated with a twist grip on the end of the handle. In a comparison test carried out on an aluminium wing, we found that the automatic punch produced less distortion in the surrounding area than the conventional punch — a useful point to note.

7
When drilling, secure both sheets together, and then the whole lot tightly to the edge of the bench.

8
You will find this technique quoted in every repair and maintenance book ever written, but it's still worth mentioning here. When drilling on a painted surface, first lay down several strips of overlapping masking tape, mark your point, punch it and then drill through with a pilot drill (i.e. a drill several sizes smaller than the final hole). The tapes prevent slipping.

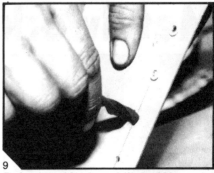

9
De-burring with a large drill should be carried out as a matter of course on every freshly drilled hole.

10
Sheet pins provide an ideal way of fastening the two sheets together once they have been drilled, and before they are riveted.

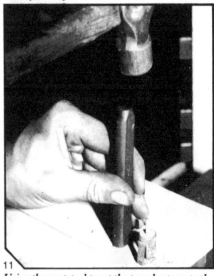

11
Using the snap tool to set the two sheets on to the head of the rivet has to be done on a hard surface such as a vice or a block. If a panel on a car has to be riveted, a dolly will need to be held behind the panel by another person to provide the solid base.

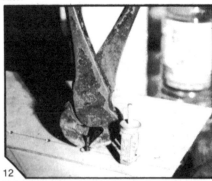

12
Trim the tail so that the length that is left protruding is about 1½ times the diameter of the rivet. This, as a general rule, leaves enough material so that when it is 'closed', a secure fastening is achieved.

Metalworking Part 4

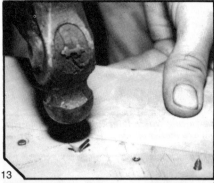

13

Bifurcated rivets should be opened initially with the blade of a screw driver, and then flattened out with a hammer. This is obviously not the most secure breed of rivet but to enhance its effect, it is a good idea to make its hole a little on the small side so that it is a tight fit. This type of rivet is ideally suited as a trim fastener, and is also useful because it is easily removed.

14

The famous Pop rivet is inserted into the hand tool as shown, and then the head of the rivet is passed through the hole in the sheet. Repeated squeezing of the handles pulls the central pin back through the head, and so flattens it. Finally the pin 'pops' off and the rivet is set.

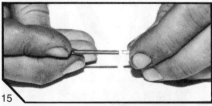

15

Drive screws have at their base a short length of plain shaft, and it is the diameter of this that determines the drill size needed to make the hole to accommodate them.

nient alternative to the somewhat clumsy hand clamps — which can be used when the riveting starts — is a clever little device known as a sheet pin. This can be pushed through any of the holes, and once tightened, will secure the two sheets together.

16

Inserting a drive screw requires just a few blows from the hammer. The wider threaded part of the shaft is forced to cut in as it goes, and this makes it a very secure fastening. Drive screws are extremely hard and so once they are in place, they are most difficult to remove. Because of this it is unwise to use them for anything but the most permanent of fixtures. They are excellent for fixing chassis and engine plates, and for attaching skins to a frame.

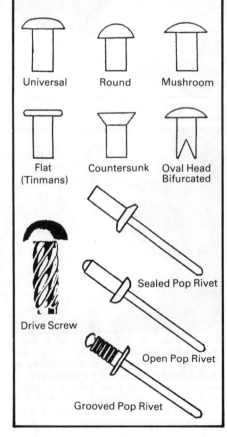

Universal   Round   Mushroom

Flat (Tinmans)   Countersunk   Oval Head Bifurcated

Drive Screw

Sealed Pop Rivet

Open Pop Rivet

Grooved Pop Rivet

The act of riveting

Rivets come in all shapes and sizes, and are made from many different types of metal. The main criterion governing the choice of metal is its softness, the rivet has to be malleable enough to be formed. So in general, rivets are made from metals such as aluminium, brass, soft iron, galvanised iron and copper. The table shown here illustrates the major types of rivet available.

Basically, there are four ways in which rivets are fastened, but all achieve the same result — the rivet having been pushed through the hole, is expanded to grip the components tightly together. Pop rivets rely on a pin (which runs right through the rivet head) being pulled out so flattening the head, bifurcated rivets push through and are then simply opened out like paper fasteners; explosive rivets carry a charge which expands the head once heat is applied and the rest rely on the use of a snap tool. All rivets are supplied having been annealed to enhance their softness, but once they have been set they become work hardened to form a permanent fixture.

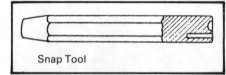

Snap Tool

The snap tool, a diagram of which is shown here, is used in the following way. With the two sheets of metal tightly clamped together, the rivet is pushed through the hole. The head of the rivet is then rested on a hard surface (such as a vice or a block), and the cylindrical moulding on the tool is fitted over the tail of the rivet — obviously the respective sizes of the snap tool and the rivet have to match. A couple of firm strikes with the hammer beds the metal sheets on to the rivet head, and then the rivet is ready for 'closing'. To do this any excess tail length has first to be removed. As a general rule you should allow 1½ times the diameter of the rivet to protrude, this should then provide enough length to successfully secure the joint. Too great a length and the rivet will bend, and too short a length will be insufficient for a secure fastening.

Opinion appears to differ over the most effective method of removing the tail. The official line is that they should be cut off neatly using a junior hack saw; however Steve was happy to simply snip them off and this seemed to produce acceptable results. This cut end is then slightly rounded with the ball of the hammer, and then the setting part of the snap tool is placed on top. A few sharp blows are enough to create the neatly formed finished rivet. □

Our thanks go to The Rivet Supply Company Ltd, Power Works, Power Road, Chiswick, London W4 5PP. Tel: 01-994 8484 for the generous selection of rivets which they donated for us to play with.

Metalworking

Part 5

Later in this metalworking series I hope to deal with each of the major welding, brazing and soldering techniques on an individual basis. However, the purpose of this months' feature is to provide a beginners guide to these topics, in preparation for the more specialised articles that are to follow.

Having dealt last month with some of the mechanical methods for joining metal, it seems sensible this time to move on to methods which involve heat and fusion. Advances have come thick and fast in this area, especially on the electrical side of things. The range of electrical welders (arc, MIG and spot) is continually being expanded, uprated and improved. The gas equipment on the other hand has not experienced such development, although this is perhaps understandable as the technology involved is a lot simpler.

Basically, the energy needed for welding with gas comes from the combustion of two gases, oxygen and acetylene. The two gases are fed from their respective cylinders, via a regulator, to the torch. The torch contains a mixing chamber where the gases come together in the desired proportions – these proportions depend upon the materials being welded, but this will be dealt with more fully at a later date.

From this chamber the mixture passes out through the nozzle where it is ignited. There are many varying types and sizes of nozzle available and all have different applications. The flame is used to heat the two parent metals until they become molten and fuse together. The effectiveness of the weld is enhanced by the use of a filler wire, which is melted simultaneously in the flame and fed into the 'weld pool' as it progresses along the joint. The filler wire is commonly made from mild steel with a copper coating, the purpose of which is to cut down oxidation. Any amount of oxidation poses a serious threat to the strength of the weld, for it leads to porosity which in turn causes the weld to become brittle. The alternative to using a filler wire involves a technique known as 'running in'. Here the parent metals are melted to form the weld pool, and this is then 'blown' along the joint with the flame and no filler wire is used. There is however, no real guarantee that the

weld will penetrate the full depth of the joint using this method, and there is a real tendency just to skim across the top of the joint. Using a filler wire is the only reliable technique.

An oxy-acetylene set-up in a workshop is undoubtedly a very versatile tool as its uses extend beyond normal welding to include brazing, lead loading and cutting. In both brazing and lead loading, where the parent metals are not melted, the gas torch is used simply as a heat source. The cutting is achieved with the aid of a special nozzle, an example of which is illustrated here.

The other way of producing sufficient heat to initiate a weld is to use electricity, and in particular, a spark jumping between two

electrodes known as an arc.

The technique that first springs to mind when thinking along these lines os of course, arc welding. This is often considered to be the most basic of the electrical methods, and indeed, it is possible to obtain a complete 'ready to go' arc welding kit for a very modest outlay.

The system is based upon a transformer with a simple current control. This adjusts the level of the amps flowing which equates directly to the heat provided. A return lead runs from the transformer and is clamped to the work, and another lead features the electrode holder. Arc welders use consumable electrodes (the equivalent of the filler rod in gas welding), and the arc is created between

Joining metals using heat — Chris Graham introduces the common methods, some typical equipment and the safety precautions needed.

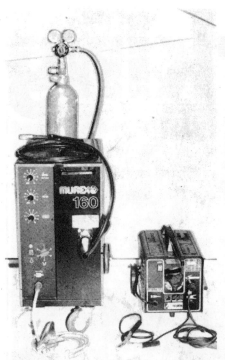

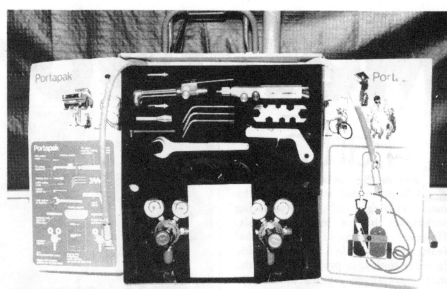

The Murex Portapak provides a good entry into the oxy-acetylene market. The kit includes a torch, hoses, regulators, pipes, a trolly etc, and costs about £214. Of course you still have to add to this the price of the bottles. Five year rental from BOC Ltd costs £80 plus the cost of the gas.

On the left is the Murex 160 MIG welder which retails for around £490 plus VAT. To this however, you have to add the following before you are ready to weld. A cylinder of shielding gas which can only be obtained direct from BOC Ltd (details from your welding suppliers). An R-type cylinder (which lasts Steve for about six months) can be obtained for a rental of £70 for five years, the gas refills cost £7.95 and there is a delivery charge of £5.60. Regulators cost about £34 and a 15Kg reel of copper coated MIG wire costs £30 (0.6mm).

At the other end of the scale there is the comparatively inexpensive imported arc welder (on the right). This comes as a package and retails at £45. A Carbon Arc brazing accessory is available for this unit, it costs £22.

This is the Murex DC130 Tradesman Arc welder. It works off a 240V input, is cooled by a fan can accomodate any type of arc electrode. It too is sold as a package and costs around £295.

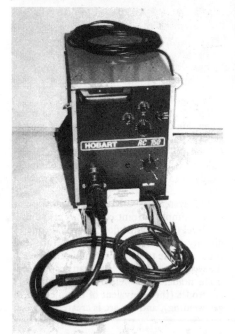

The Mobart RC150 provides an interesting alternative to the Murex kit, although it is a little more expensive at £525 plus VAT.

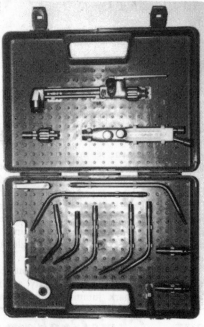

This is an example of a torch and nozzle kit. The Murex Saffire 3 set will cost you £138, but the hoses and regulators are still extra.

this and the work when it is brought close — it completes the circuit. To actually begin welding you have to 'strike the arc' against the job in a similar fashion to striking a match. Once the arc is fired it has to be kept at the correct length and angle and moved at the correct speed if a successful weld is to be obtained, and this takes practice.

The electrode rods are coated in flux which provides a protective umbrella for the arc as it burns, to prevent oxidation. Once the weld has set the flux can be chipped from the surface to reveal the clean result. It is possible however, to trap the flux in the weld — a problem created by incorrect electrode angle — and this leads to porosity. It causes holes which cannot be re-covered so the whole lot has to be ground back and re-layed.

A development of the same theory produced MIG welding — Metal Inert Gas, which can be described as arc welding without the flux. In MIG welding the job of protecting the arc and the weld pool is entrusted to an inert gas that is released from the handset as the welding takes place. MIG welders are considerably more sophisticated than their cheaper arc relatives, and the result is a more versatile piece of equipment. A continuous stream of wire is fed to the handset via an electric motor controlled by a trigger. The inert gas (usually Argon) is supplied from a separate cylinder and is regulated by a solenoid that is also linked to the trigger, and so stops as and when the wire does. Like the arc welder, the MIG has a return lead that has to be set up in a similar way before the welding can commence. The final control to be provided by the trigger is the on/off switch for the power itself, so that once the wire speed and gas flow have been set, the trigger is all that need be operated. As a result the MIG is more controllable than the arc and it produces a very localised heat. The particular advantage of this is that it enables it to be used safely close to door rubbers, carpets and painted areas, with the minimum risk of fire or distortion.

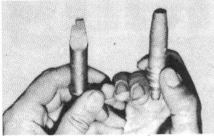

This picture shows the difference between a standard nozzle and one designed specifically for cutting (left). The cutting nozzle is stepped so that it can be rested on the metal and drawn along accurately as it cuts.

Goggles are an essential parts of the welders' tool kit — they provide protection against harmful ultra violet rays as well as from flying metal and sparks. The pair on the right feature a window action that converts them from green filter to clear glass. Goggles range in price from £3 to £7 depending on the type chosen.

Anti-Spatter spray is a particularly useful pre-welding treatment. It prevents the globules of molten metal thrown up by the process from sticking too permanently to the surfaces on to which they fall. The spray should be available for about £4 a bottle.

This regulator has been fitted with a Flashback arrester, the purpose of which is to prevent any burn-back reaching the regulator and cylinder. This can be caused by small explosions at the torch which create a back pressure up the hose. The device works as a one way valve and only allows the gas out of the cylinder. The slightest pressure in the opposite direction trips the valve. Flashback arresters cost about £50.

(Continued)

A spot welder is a little more specialised in both its construction and its application. It relies on the resistance that is created by the parent metals as the current is passed between the two electrodes. This resistance generates sufficient heat to fuse the metal together, and the process is further improved by the pinching action of the electrodes. There is virtually no distortion created and no welding rods are needed. It produces a very neat job although its applications are limited. In many cases special electrode arms have to be obtained for individual jobs and these are expensive and often can only be used for that one task alone. This factor tends to make spot welders a little impractical for the DIY user unless of course he is doing a long and repetitive run to make it worthwhile.

Safety

This is an aspect of all welding and heat treatment processes that we feel is often understressed. Obviously anything involving high pressure flames or an electric arc is potentially dangerous. If the appropriate safety measures are taken and common sense applied, the risks will be minimised. Protective clothing is probably the most obvious precaution to employ against accident. Gloves, cotton overalls (nylon overalls should be avoided as they will melt, stick and burn if provoked) and goggles or a face shield are all essential.

All forms of welding but especially arc and MIG, give off strong ultra violet rays, and these can quickly damage the retina of the eye. It is vital to choose goggles of the correct filtration so that they provide suitable protection — relevant information is usually supplied with the unit, but failing this, your local stockist will certainly be qualified to advise. Goggles are also a sensible precaution when chipping the hardened flux from an arc weld, although clear rather than green ones are preferable! Another point worth noting with regard to arc welders is that they can overheat. Many of the units on the market today feature a built in cut-out mechanism which limits their continuous use capability. It is worth checking for this feature before purchase. Spatter is an unfortunate companion of arc welding, and you will find that certain rods are particularly prone to it. Molten globules are thrown out from the weld pool as the weld is made and this is both irritating and damaging. There are, on the market, anti-spatter sprays which we definitely recommend. The spray should be used on the surrounding areas and on any tools that may be affected, and it will significantly aid the removal of the hardened globules once they have cooled.

Gas welding creates its own special problems, not the least of which is localised pollution. If you are gas welding in a confined space ensure that there is adequate ventilation for it only takes a very small percentage of escaped gas in the atmosphere to create the risk of an explosion. It is also worth remembering that the flame does spread and that the heat produced is not nearly as localised as it is

with arc or MIG welding. A sizable area should always be cleared around the point to be welded. Carpets, window and sealing rubbers etc are the obvious examples of flammable materials, but also bear in mind that substances such as underseal melt, catch fire and drip, which can be unpleasant and dangerous if you are working under the car. As a simple rule it is always a good idea to turn off the gas once you have finished a weld, as moving the torch away to inspect your handywork can have disastrous effects on nearby headlinings, painted panels and vinyl seat coverings. Even lifting your goggles with the lighted torch in one hand can prove expensive. One final problem that can occur with gas equipment is 'flash back'. This problem will be dealt with more fully in later articles, but basically what happens is that the gas burns back up the hoses towards the cylinders. A device known as a flashback arrester is a desirable precaution against this unpleasant happening.

I would like to bring this month's feature to a close with a few words of wisdom from Steve, concerning welding for beginners. He suggests that MIG welding is the 'easiest' to learn, gas is the most satisfying and versatile, arc is probably best left for the domestic jobs around the house and spot welding is a little too specialised for the home market. Finally I would like to thank Crawley Welding Supplies Limited (11 Royce Road, Fleming Way Industrial Centre, Crawley, Sussex, telephone (0293) 29761/2) for their help in the preparation of this article. □

Metalworking

Part 6

I feel honour bound to confess here and now that so far my only real experience of soldering involved some rather dodgy repairs made to some even dodgier Scalextric cars, many years ago. Casting my mind back even further, to those halcyon days spent in the school metalwork shop, I dimly remember being told about "these 'ere irons". The objects in question had elderly and mis-shapen wooden handles, long metal shafts and then at the tip, a large lump of what appeared to be rusty metal. They were certainly not my idea of an iron especially as the heads were actually made of copper. So it was with great interest that I, together with Steve Demol, launched into this month's feature, the results of which are recounted to you here.

The iron is in fact the solderer's most important tool. It is the device that once heated, is used to transfer the molten solder on to the job, where it sets hard to secure the joint. The head of the iron is made from copper for the following two reasons. Copper is a first class conductor of heat and also allows its surface to become easily 'tinned' (a process that will be explained later). Special soldering stoves are available for heating the irons, but it is possible to achieve satisfactory results using the flame from a domestic gas cooker. It is important to guard

1

To simply join the two sheets of plate together (as in the construction of tubular housing etc), a sweat joint is the ideal solution. First the two plates involved should be coated in solder paint (or tinned in the conventional manner) to cover the touching surfaces.

against overheating as this causes a bit to become pitted and unsatisfactory for use. If this does happen, the bit has to be filed smooth once again. When heating the irons in a flame watch out for a green colour, as this is generally accepted as indicating the correct temperature.

Flux is a very necessary addition to the process as it helps the solder to flow smoothly and protects the surfaces that are to be joined. As with welding, oxidation is a deadly enemy of the soldered joint. Fluxes are available in liquid form, or as a powder or paste, whose melting point is always lower than that of the solder. The final ingredient of course, is the solder itself which is also available in several types. These varieties are mainly determined by the type of work being done. For example there is cored solder which comes impregnated with flux and is particularly suitable for electrical component work done with a small electric iron. The soft solders are based upon a tin/lead

The act of brazing has to be treated with respect in terms of safety. Goggles should be worn (and gloves too — we must remind Steve — but not nylon clothing) and it should only be attempted in a well ventilaged room. Brazing overhead is not a good idea as gravity easily overpowers capillary attraction.

alloy and it is the proportion of tin within the alloy that determines the quality – the higher the percentage of tin, the better the quality – it runs very freely. Steve says that you can actually hear a good solder!. If it is flexed and little cracking sounds can be heard, the solder contains a high percentage of tin which gives it fine qualities. However, the king of the solders is silver solder, which is expensive but much stronger, and works at a lower temperature. It is made from an alloy of copper, tin and silver and is used on window frames and radiators on older cars.

Chris Graham looks into the theories, methods and applications of both soldering and brazing.

The process of tinning is the most important stage involved in soldering, and if it is not done correctly then a successful joint will not be possible. To begin with the area that is to be tinned (the iron, the work, or both) must be thoroughly cleaned, and this means to a shiny metal finish. A thin layer of solder has then to be laid down on to the clean surface. This is achieved by applying a mixture of flux and solder to the hot surface, then wiping away any excess with a clean grease free cloth (not a nylon cloth as it will melt), to produce a mirror like finish. Be careful when wiping to avoid rubbing through the skin layer and so breaking the seal, as if this occurs the subject will have to be cleaned again, and the process repeated.

The idea behind the tinning process is to

2
With the two plates tightly positioned together (clamps provide the ideal answer), an extra strip of solder paint should be added along the edge of the joint. At this stage you must ensure that both plates are completely tight against one another. If they are not, un-clamp the plates, clean off the paint, alter the plates as necessary, then start all over again.

3
A domestic blow torch of the DIY paint stripping variety will be quite sufficient as a heat source. The joint should be heated until the solder paint begins to turn silver. This is an indication that the correct temperature has been reached and that the solder is starting to run throughout the joint.

ensure that the solder which is added to produce the bond, is able to run smoothly over all the surfaces involved in the joint. Without this ability it simply will not work. It is wise to 'tin' over at least twice the area that will be needed for the joint, and to waste as little time as possi-

4
With the solder rod in one hand and the blow torch (at a distance) in the other, a run of solder can be laid down along the joint. This should not be too thick but if it is, it should be quickly wiped away with a clean grease free cloth. Further gentle heating will see the excess solder drawn into the joint and if the plates are turned over, oozing out from the other side. By this stage the joint has been well and truly penetrated and should be allowed to cool.

5
Because the heat required for brazing is fairly great, a fire brick is a sensible idea as a base to work on. Obviously the size of the job being undertaken determines the number required and in some cases, a complete hearth will need to be constructed. In this example we chose to braze a stainless steel tube on to a couple of mild steel blocks. It is of course vitally important that all surfaces be thoroughly cleaned, and then the local area can begin to be heated.

ble in between the cleaning and the tinning stages, and between tinning and finishing the job, to minimise the risk of atmospheric contamination. Also, never handle a freshly cleaned sample with bare hands as the grease naturally present in the skin will upset the process. Cleaning in most cases will involve a wire brush and white spirit, but in more severe examples where rust is present, a file may have

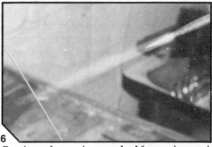

6
Brazing rods come in a standard form or in a variety known as the pre-flux rod. This variety already contains the flux required, which eliminates the time consuming need for the continual dipping into the flux, of the conventional rod. To start with the rod itself (an ordinary brazing rod in this case) was given a short burst from the flame, which was then returned to heating the work.

7
The heated rod is then dipped into the flux (powdered in this case) so that the end becomes coated.

to be used.

The tinned surfaces are then ready to be joined by the addition of more solder. The heated iron is used to melt the fresh solder, and at the same time heat the joint into which the molten solder is to run. A point worth considering here is the type of joint being used. The soldered joint does not provide the most secure of fixings and therefore, it is a good idea to maximise the joint area. The introduction of flanges provides a simple and effective solution, but stepped lap joints can be equally useful. The close proximity of the two surfaces being joined produces an effect known as capillary attraction, by which the molten solder is drawn deep into the joint to seal it fully.

Note that when tinning a surface which is sloping or even vertical it is best to start at the lower end and work upwards thus fully using the heat (which rises).

For our example, we chose to demonstrate a technique known as the sweated joint. This type of joint is best suited to situations where large areas have to be secured, or where the job is too small for the use of a soldering iron at all. The idea is that both surfaces are tinned, then clamped tightly together (it is essential that a precise fit is achieved) and heated, in order that the solder should run. A particularly useful aid to this end is a product known as Solder Paint. It is a liquid that contains both solder and flux, and it neatly achieves the tinning process.

Brazing

Brazing is a little like the elder brother of soldering. Its results are a lot stronger than soldering, and yet it still relies upon the same basic

principles. As with soldering, in brazing neither of the parent metals are melted, a flux is used and the braze is drawn into the joint thanks to capillary attraction. Probably the fundamental difference between the two is that brazing is achieved at a much higher temperature. Brazing can be used to fasten two like or two unlike metals, and this is one of its major advantages, as it makes it versatile should the situation demand it.

However, due to the higher temperatures involved (brazing rods melt at around 950°C, soft solders melt at around 200°C), brazing requires the use of a gas torch to produce the heat. But having said that, there is still less heat distortion involved than there is with gas welding, and another advantage is that the final braze is far less brittle than an equivalent weld. This makes it particularly suitable for joints that will have to withstand a certain degree of flexing such as on certain body panels (or bicycle frames). However, it is not advisable to braze car chassis. Our endeavours are illustrated in the picture series. □

8

It is essential that the two parent metals are made hot enough to melt the brazing rod when it is touched on. It is no good melting the rod in the flame and then dabbing it on, as the braze will immediately re-set having achieved nothing. Whilst the braze is being laid down the flame should be played all around the area, not just at one single point. To begin with we found the brick was absorbing too much heat from the metal, which was preventing the necessary level being reached. Simply raising the work off the surface cured this effectively.

9

The flux sets to a black solid on the braze as it cools, but this is easily removed by quenching (cooling the work rapidly in water). In cases such as these where a tube is to be quenched, avoid plunging it straight into a bucket or trough of water as the steam produced can be funnelled up the tube to cause painful burns. The sensible answer is to use a hose.

10

The finished braze having been cleaned provides a reasonably presentable joint.

NEXT MONTH
Lead loading.

CONTINUED FROM PAGE 21

Metalworking Part 1 _____ Continued

folds are more easily made using a proprietory metal folder; the only limitation of this type of tool is the width of metal which it will accommodate. The smaller folders which are readily available to the home restorer can handle sheets of metal 24″ wide and prices vary widely from as little as £30 to £100.

It is worth considering whether you could avoid such expense by improvising. Metal can be folded easily by clamping it between two stout pieces of timber (or, better still, thick angle iron) in a strong vice, preferably a large engineers vice which will allow sufficient depth to accommodate a few inches of metal on one side of the fold. The metal is then folded by hammering it over using a leather mallet, or by holding a piece of hardwood against the metal and striking this with an ordinary metal hammer, the idea being to fold the metal against the angle iron without creating local distortion. It is advisable to use clamps to hold the pieces of timber together on each side of the sheet of metal (clamps or Mole grips or similar would do if you were using angle iron) so that the whole assembly can be moved along in the vice as hammering progresses without losing the line of the fold. It is as well to restrict the hammering to not more than a few inches on each side of the vice where the timbers or angle iron

Specialised tools are also available to the amateur of which this Edge Setter (number 042500) from Sykes-Pickavant is one example. This is used for creating the slight 'step' along the edge of a panel so that it can be overlapped against the adjacent panel for subsequent lap or spot welding.

will be unable to separate, in this way you should get sharp neat folds.

Safety

It is appropriate that in the first of a series of articles about metalworking equipment and techniques we should strongly recommend safety measures to be adopted in the workshop. We will return to this topic as necessary to emphasise measures which are particularly relevant to specific tasks such as welding etc, but to start with you would be well advised to obtain a stout pair of leather gloves (from the local Motor Factor) for handling and cutting metal in order to avoid the nasty injuries which can be inflicted by sharp and often jagged edges. The gloves will be needed for almost all metalworking tasks and you will also need goggles to protect your eyes from flying debris, sparks etc, when using power tools. Buy a good pair of overalls too, not nylon, which will be destroyed by sparks etc, but a pair containing a high percentage of cotton. □

Next Month
Basic panel beating.

Metalworking

We must be honest: you don't become an expert at lead loading overnight and it requires rather more preparation and more effort than plastic filling does — which is why it's comparatively rare these days. But its advantages remain constant — it's more durable than plastic filler, it adheres better, is more resistant to rust, and absorbs knocks and flexing better.

The technique can be learned however, even though George Martin in the pictures made it look much easier than it is — you'll find at first that a fair amount of your precious solder ends on the floor! Try it all out on small, horizontal areas first; George says the key thing is to get to know how the lead moves and what heat to apply to make it plas-

1

Tools of the trade: a craftsman usually builds up a kit to suit his own needs. This home-made tray contains tallow, solder sticks, variety of hardwood blocks, moleskin, a steel scraper and a crocodile clip to hold the sticks with. Equipment varies from person to person though.

Part 7 — *Lead loading – Paul Skilleter went along to Martin Robey Ltd to learn what it's all about!*

2

Thorough cleaning of the surface to eliminate all dirt, corrosion and contamination is essential otherwise the tinning, to be applied next, won't adhere properly. A selection of wire brushes to suit the various contours and cavities are used first, in conjunction with an electric drill.

3

To reduce welds and get rid of heavy corrosion an abrasive disc is also used, for instance in the E-type's door aperture where the rubber seal will eventually seat. You can also spot a couple of dents on top of the scuttle which is one reason for the filling process apart from the panel joins.

4

The final clean-up is carried out by orbital sander used over the entire area of the repair surface, and beyond. It's a good idea at this stage to check with a straight-edge for overlooked high spots which will need reducing with a panel hammer. Wire brush any sunken areas the sanding disc has missed.

Next, the lead or solder paint is brushed on; this is quite expensive but must be well brushed into all crevices. Again, apply over a wider area than you actually anticipate lead loading. Note that door and bonnet are best removed while cleaning and applying the solder paint.

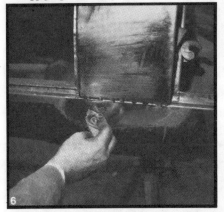

To tin, play your flame over the paint, seven or eight square inches at a time, and as the surface changes (it begins to 'pickle') wipe it in one positive sweep with a cotton (not nylon) cloth. This removes impurities brought to the surface by chemicals in the paint, and leaves a bright tinned surface.

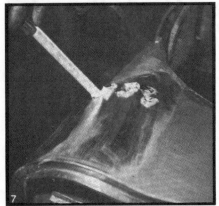

Flame is applied to the stick, and to the tinned surface underneath, though not enough to quite liquify either. Solder is deposited on the tinned metal by a quick twisting motion as the end of the stick softens; don't press too hard though. About three sticks of solder were used on this job, incidentally, and some 30 for the whole shell.

tic but not runny.

George didn't, but he advises the use of gloves (preferably leather); nylon overalls

Depositing the solder on vertical surfaces is rather more difficult, because you have gravity to contend with. On an E-type, door and bonnet gaps are achieved by lead so both front and rear edges of bulkhead are covered. This also serves to cover ripples which spot-welding is inclined to leave.

Now the really tricky part begins. Melt the surface of the tallow, dip your block into it, apply heat to a few lumps of deposited lead – enough to soften it but not to make it run – and try smoothing the lumps out. Practice on a horizontal panel first.

Real skill is needed to obtain a good edge on a vertical surface like this, the difficulty being to heat the lead enough for it to be moved, without it running away in a silver stream or series of droplets. Watch for the lead to 'sweat' as you apply the flame – it's then ready. Ronson blow-torch or welding torch are suitable heat sources.

and plastic shoes should be avoided, and never use anything except a coarse file to reduce the lead — the dust is very definitely not to be inhaled. Best to keep the kids away

Don't attempt to achieve a totally smooth surface at first, just get it covered. Move the lead around to fill depressions, keeping fairly generous amounts of tallow on the block. Don't try and 'catch' small runs as you may end up losing larger areas. Note that door has been replaced to check contours and gaps.

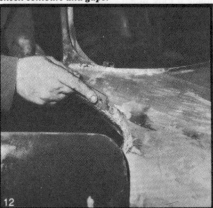

Now comes the hardest part! A dreadnought file is used to reduce the surface, including corners, though surface is first wiped with white spirit to remove tallow. The procedure is as per plastic filler basically, and straight-edge as well as the hand can be used to check for depressions.

It takes about two days to file-off a lead-loaded E-type shell; you'll find your shoulders ache too. You can add lead but any exposed metal must be re-tinned first. If leaving overnight, wipe off with white spirit as chemicals in the solder paint make steel go rusty in adjacent areas.

from the solder sticks and shavings too. All the effort and preparation are worthwhile though, when at last you can sit back and admire your final, shining surface. □

Metalworking

Part 8

Flashback, leftward, carbonising and rightward are just some of the interesting words that help to make up a gas welder's vocabulary. His more staple set of sayings are equally interesting but, I fear, are unsuitable for publication in the decorous pages of this journal. However, in the following columns I shall pick my way through the subject to provide a useful and wholesome account of the equipment, the techniques and the dangers involved in the gas welder's art.

The basic principle which makes gas welding possible is that when two (or more) closely aligned pieces of like metal are heated to their melting points, the molten liquids mix (which produces the 'weld pool'), and as the area cools, the metals become strongly fused together as one. Heat is obviously the essential ingredient in this process, though it is not the only influencing factor. Different metals require flames of different compositions in order that the welding process may be achieved, and this is only one of several factors that must be considered and understood before welding commences.

The energy for the heating process is provided by the combustion of a mixture of two gases, oxygen and acetylene — hence oxyacetylene welding. The acetylene is burnt in the presence of the oxygen and is known, therefore, as the fuel gas. The two are supplied from separate cylinders via regulators and rubber hoses, to a mixing chamber in the handle of the torch. On the torch there are controls for both gases which enables the mixture of gases emerging at the nozzle to be accurately controlled. At the nozzle the gas mixture is ignited to produce

Oxygen + acetylene = Heat.
Chris Graham outlines the rudiments
of gas welding.

the finely tuned flame which in its neutral condition (equal amounts of oxygen and acetylene) reaches a temperature of some 2800°C.

The regulator on each cylinder is secured by large brass fixings, and accomodates two dials. The right hand one of the two indicates the cylinder contents, and the other reads the outlet pressure. Each regulator has a pressure

regulating screw which is operated once the main valve on the cylinder has been opened. To avoid confusion and accident a colour coding system is employed which ensures that all oxygen cylinders are painted black, and the acetylene cylinders painted maroon. Further precautions include differing colours for the rubber hoses connecting the cylinders with the torch, and the controls on

---

The equipment.

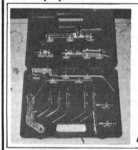

A/B

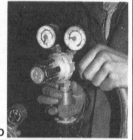

C/D

A. A typical example of the sort of nozzle kit now on the market. A set this size will cost in the region of £60.
B. The nozzles are screwed into the hand torch, which features separate controls for the oxygen

and the acetylene pressures.
C. Nozzle cleaners are essential tools if the equipment is to be maintained correctly. However, they should not be used too enthusiastically as they do wear away the nozzle.

D. The regulator must be in good order for it to be completely safe. Threads and seals should be checked thoroughly and often, and if accidentally dropped, the regulator should be inspected by experts.

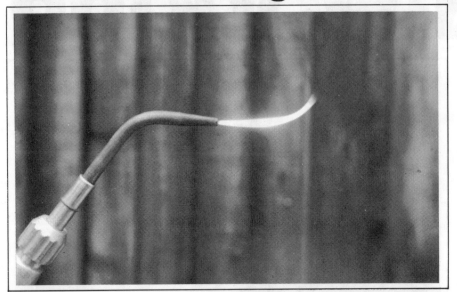

the torch (blue for oxygen and red for acetylene). Even colour blindness is partially guarded against as all the fittings associated with the acetylene supply have left hand threads, and this is indicated by small cuts on the angles of all relevant nuts.

The nozzles that are fitted to the torch come in a variety of sizes, and it is these which determine the thickness of metal that can be welded. The common sizes are: 1,2,3,4,5,7,10,13,18,25 and 35, and the larger the number, the larger the nozzle size. The No. 1 nozzle for example is best suited to welding metal that is up to 0.9mm thick, and so this makes it most useful for general body work repairs. For the heavier gauges of metal

Light the torch with just the acetylene switched on, and adjust the pressure to the point at which the flame just ceases to smoke. The oxygen can then be introduced and the balance altered to achieve the desired flame.

such as those used on chassis (up to 2.0mm thick), a No. 2 or 3 will be required. With commercially marketed nozzle kits an information chart is usually supplied which gives details concerning the nozzle sizes and their suitability for welding and cutting various gauges of metal. However, the figures given on these tables are only intended to act as a guide. In practice, they vary according to conditions such as the flame setting, the material and the hose diameter etc.

In some cases, for example when attempting an edge weld, simply melting the parent metals will be sufficient to join them and there will be no need for any further metal

When you are gas welding thin metal sheet the heat from the torch is liable to provoke distortion. A precaution that should be taken to reduce the distorting effects is to tack the joint before finally welding it. The thinner the subject metal is, the closer the tacks should be positioned.

addition. However in joints where there is a gap to be filled (such as one with bevelled edges), there is a definite need for fresh metal to be added, and in such situations a filler rod is required. Today these rods are commonly made from mild steel with a copper coating (the copper helps reduce oxidation). They are fed into the molten 'weld pool' as the weld progresses and the rate at which this is done determines the penetration of the weld, and its final appearance. Generally speaking the size of rod most commonly used for everyday workshop use is 1.6mm (in diameter). Such rods are often sold by weight, and are available from all welding suppliers.

Using gas equipment

Before you start welding a certain amount of preparation of the area is required. It is wise

Gas welding can produce a reasonably neat finish.

to remove any dirt, old paint, underseal and flaky rust from the areas that are to be joined. Although the standards of cleanliness are not as high as those required for MIG welding (a bright and shiny surface is not essential), it is obviously a good idea to get it as clean as possible. The torch will happily weld through limited amounts of debris but this will be accompanied by spitting and spluttering. Problems may also occur when welding in confined spaces which may lead to gas build-ups. The angle of the torch and adequate ventilation will help however. Such problems are avoidable if the area is cleaned thoroughly beforehand. Now you can set up the equipment.

Before screwing the regulators on to their respective cylinders, it is sensible to 'vent' each valve first. This is simply done using the bottle key and allowing a *short* sharp burst of gas to escape from the open valve to clear it. Sometimes foreign particles can get lodged in the top of the valve, so venting is the simple answer (remember not to smoke a cigarette or lean over the valve at the same time). With the main valves clear, the regulators can be attached although care is needed at this stage to avoid cross-threading the fixings. Never use a hammer to tighten or loosen any part of the assembly, the palm of the hand on the correct spanner should be quite adequate. The correct spanner is also important as using an alternative such as mole grips or pliers can round off the nuts which can lead to a weakened seal. The hoses and the torch are connected next and the main cylinder valves can then be opened. Most modern regulators have markings on the gauges which indicate recommended pressure settings for certain tasks (welding and cutting etc) and these are set next with the aid of the pressure regulating screw. Once set the torch valves can then be opened and the levels re-adjusted accordingly, and then the torch is ready for lighting.

With the acetylene control open slightly the torch can be lit. It will burn with a yellow flame which, if the pressure is too great, will give off black smoke. It should be adjusted until the flame is in contact with the end of the nozzle and it reaches the point where it just ceases to smoke, and then the oxygen control can be opened.

As the pressure of oxygen increases a white cone will become clearly visible in the centre of the flame. This should be regulated until it is only a matter of millimetres long and shows a rounded tip, indicating that the flame is in a neutral state. From this point the flame can then be adjusted to cater for the job in hand because, as was outlined earlier, different metals require different types of flame to weld them. To produce an oxidising flame the acetylene flow must be reduced slightly, which will in turn reduce the overall size of the flame and its central cone. This type of flame is required for welding brasses and bronzes. The carburising flame (or reducing

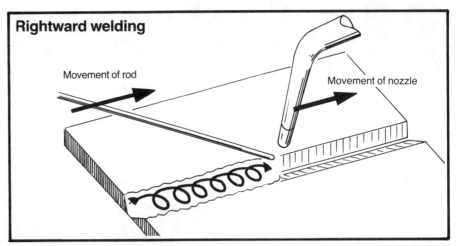

Rightward welding

Movement of rod

Movement of nozzle

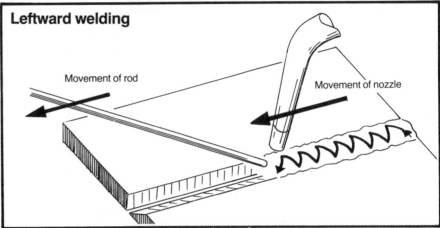

Leftward welding

Movement of rod

Movement of nozzle

flame) is needed when cast iron is to be welded, and is produced by increasing the acetylene flow until a feather like haze can be seen around the central cone. For other materials such as steel, stainless steel, aluminium and copper, the neutral flame is the ideal choice.

There are two main methods of welding and the choice is determined by the thickness of the metal to be joined. Generally speaking, if the pieces to be welded are less than 5.00mm thick, as they are in most car work, the Leftward method should be adopted in which the weld proceeds from right to left along the joint. The torch should be kept moving at all times, but as well as the forward movement, there should be a slight zig-zag movement. This will ensure that both sides of the joint are kept suitably molten as the weld progresses. At the same time of course, the filler wire needs to be fed in to build up the body of the weld. The real trick appears to be to keep your eye on the very centre of the weld pool and ensure that it is maintained. With practice it should be possible to hold the weld pool in a 'topped up' state as it moves along the joint, thus ensuring a satisfactory weld. The Rightward method of welding as you have probably already guessed, involves the weld moving from left to right. The filler rod is moved in circular movements along behind the torch and

although this method is quicker and a little more economical, it is only applied to metal that is over 5.00mm thick, and so need not really concern us further.

The major problem that runs hand in hand with gas welding is heat distortion, and the thinner the subject, the greater are its effects. One precaution that can be taken to help reduce the effects of this distortion is to tack the joint prior to the final weld. The tacks should be made as neat and as small as possible because they can provide annoying obstructions to weld over if they are too large. On fine work with thin sheet metal the tacking is a very important part of the process, and should be set close together, but on thicker subjects the spacing can be greater.

Safety

When dealing with a mixture of two highly flammable gases which are stored under pressure, there are bound to be risks involved and the first one to mention is pollution. The danger here is from the acetylene which apart from being foul smelling, is explosive even in very small proportions. Therefore it is essential that gas welding should only be attempted in a well ventilated workshop.

All equipment needs to be kept clean and free from blockages that may lead to pressure build-ups. Any perished or split rubber hoses or 'O' ring seals should be discarded without

CONTINUED ON PAGE **50**

Metalworking

Part 9

Should one of your favourite tools become bent or blunt, heat treatment may be the only alternative to consigning it to the scrap bin and buying a horribly characterless replacement. The art of heat treatment is to accurately control the temperature so as to achieve the desired effect, but more of that later.

It is perhaps wise to begin by outlining the main heat treatment processes, and what effect they actually have on the subject metal. The type of metal is important and the main processes centre around the treatment of irons and steels (although other metals can of course be effectively treated), and it is the carbon content within these two that is of great relevance here. As iron and steel are among the most commonly used metals in tool manufacture, we shall concentrate on these for this article. Therefore, the first step is to identify your metal, which in itself can cause problems for the inexperienced. If you have no knowledge of how to identify metals yourself, and there is nobody else to help, you must draw your own conclusions from a number of simple tests, as described in the table, which should provide proof for a definite identification.

A freshly treated tool such as this chisel can be tested with a gentle blow from a hammer against a suitable hard base. The chisel should of course be left unmarked.

The carbon which is present in iron combines chemically with the iron molecules in various ways which have a very definite bearing on the properties and structure of the resultant metal. To fully grasp the workings that take place within the metal under treatment requires an understanding of some fairly advanced chemical principles, which from a purely practical point of view, need not really concern us further.

Annealing

The most useful and commonly used functions of heat treatment are provided by three basic techniques — annealing, tempering and normalising. The purpose of annealing is to re-soften a piece of metal after it has been worked, and become hardened by that working. It is achieved by reducing the coarseness of the grains and removing any internal stresses which may have been created by the working. The sample is heated until it becomes cherry red (a colour which indicates a temperature of between 800-850 degrees C), when it can again be worked. But as soon as it cools the process must be repeated. The softness of the piece is ensured by a slow cooling which is important. Professionals achieve this with a furnace but the DIY person must do his best with the blow lamp or by packing it in

Metal	Sight test	Drop test (on concrete)	Saw and bend test
Cast Iron	Surface rough and grey with moulding marks	No ring (dead) — but don't *drop* it, it breaks easily.	Easy to cut once started, large crystaline structure, breaks easily
Wrought Iron	Red and scaly with evidence of rolling	A little less dull than above and sounds metallic	Cuts and bends easily, but breaks
Mild Steel	Dark mill-scale or bright when drawn	Moderate ringing	Cuts easily and bends a few times before breaking
Cast Steel	Smooth with fine but dark mill-scale	High ringing note	Quite hard to cut, hardly bends and then snaps
Alloy Steel	Bright when drawn or fine dark sheen	Moderate ringing	Impossible to cut except with a grinding wheel, breaks without bending

Chris Graham unravels the mysteries of treating metal with heat.

Metalworking Part 9

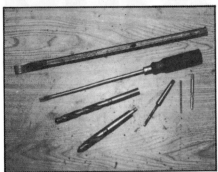

A selection of the type of tools that are most suited to basic heat treatment is shown here. Chisels, screwdrivers, punches and drills all make ideal subjects.

something such as fire clay to slow the cooling. The blacksmith working at his forge is continually making use of this technique.

Normalising

Normalising is a process that is similar in principle to annealing — in that it involves the heating and the cooling of an item, to produce a stable and stress free structure. The big difference however is the rate of cooling employed, which in normalising is much quicker than in annealing. With this technique the article is allowed to cool in the air and a reasonably 'soft' metal is the result. The ultimate condition of the sample after normalising depends upon its chemical composition (in particular its carbon content). Mild steels (which have a low carbon content) are most suited to this process, which is ideal for the treatment of freshly manufactured or worked items.

Tempering

Tempering is used as a type of finishing process to produce a useable item. The problem is that once the subject has been re-worked to effect a repair (involving the annealing process), it is quenched in order to cool it. This, at this stage, is done simply by plunging it into a container of water which cools it rapidly. As you can imagine, reducing something from red heat down to stone cold in a few seconds is quite a violent process, and it effects the structure accordingly. The metal is in effect 'frozen' into a needle-like structure which makes it extremely hard and brittle. These are obviously not properties that would be suited to a chisel for example, and therefore a further stage is required to alter this. A second heating known as tempering provides just the solution, but it is not quite as simple as before. It is no good simply re-heating the item up to red heat again and then quenching it, as this will get you nowhere. The sample must be heated to a *specific* temperature that will provide the necessary finish for the tool required and must then be quenched, and this temperature is indicated in a number of ways.

The heating of metals to an accurate temperature is quite an involved business in itself, and because it is so important, companies such as tool manufacturers spend a lot of money ensuring good results. Special furnaces are used specifically for heating accurately, and in some places baths of molten lead or lead and tin are used for large castings. It is essential that large items (and indeed small but lengthy ones) are heated evenly to avoid distortion, and such baths achieve this well. On a slightly less grand level there are various indicating paints and crayons available, which change characteristically at the desired temperature. Also available are assorted cones and pellets which fulfill the same function, only they indicate it by melting. One step further down the scale puts you in the DIY league, with the private owner tempering a faithful screwdriver having already straightened it. In this case it is unlikely that he (or she) will have a custom built forge nestling at the rear of the lock-up, and so a further method has to be relied upon.

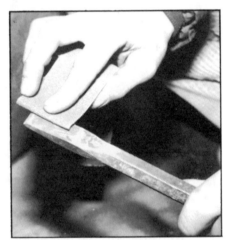

Before tempering it is important that the area to be treated is brought to a shiny finish.

Once the straightening or whatever has been achieved and the tool has been quenched, it should be cleaned so that the area to be tempered (only the tip in the case of chisels etc) exhibits a shiny surface. Then as the tempering begins and the area heats up, oxides will start to form on the freshly cleaned surface, and these will vary in colour These differing colours conveniently correspond to different temperatures, as the table shown here illustrates.

Colour of oxide	Approx. temp.°C	Applications
Pale straw	230	Scrapers, and tools for working soft metals such as brass
Dark straw	240	Tools for working mild steel
Brown	250	Shear blades, wood turning tools
Brownish purple	260	Punches, rivet snaps, wood working tools
Purple	270	Axes
Deep purple	280	Cold chisels
Blue	300	Springs

On the face of it this may seem a fairly hit and miss affair but in practice, surprisingly good results may be achieved. However, one point worth remembering is that these colours should not be viewed near to a window or in bright sunlight, as this will distort them enough to affect the result. Tempering is a very quick process and you must be ready to quench the item immediately after the colour has been reached. Achieving temperatures at the lower end of the scale needs great care as a fraction too long with the torch or blow lamp could send the temperature shooting past the limit.

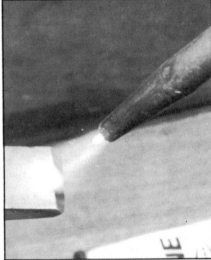

The heating is the crucial stage, especially when tempering, when characteristic colours have to be watched for.

So far I have only talked about water being used for the quenching part of the operation, however, this is not the only choice available. The speed at which the item is allowed to cool can be all important and the quenching medium chosen is used to control this. When the object is first immersed the outer layers are cooled rapidly but the inner core remains hotter for longer. This can cause problems as the outer layers contract slightly to cool and harden which in effect traps the inner core, which is still hot and wants to expand, and this can lead to cracking. In terms of the degree of severity of the quench, the mediums can be arranged in the following order; 5% caustic Soda solution, brine, cold water, warm water, mineral animal and then vegetable oil – the latter being the least severe. In some cases it is not so essential for the item to be made extremely hard above all else, in which case it can be made tougher using a gentle quench. When using the oils however, do make sure that they are not highly flammable. When quenching in water the hot metal should never be allowed to simply rest stationary, it should be agitated continually. This will prevent the build up of steam immediately around the piece which will hinder the cooling.

CONTINUED ON PAGE 50

Metalworking

Part 10

Although gas is generally regarded as the most flexible medium with which to weld, many in the DIY fraternity are bound to find it unsuitable. Some of the practical aspects that will undoubtedly influence the budding DIY welder when he comes to equip himself are cost, size, convenience and ease of use, and when these are considered with reference to oxy-acetylene equipment, the picture is not a pretty one.

The alternative however, is to fall back on electricity as a power source — the welding kit in this area being much more portable and readily available. The ubiquitous arc welder is surely known to all these days, and is available in a wide range of specifications and prices. Carbon arc attachments provide the possibility to usefully extend the ability of the arc welder into the brazing field, though you may find them a little harder to track down. Spot welding provides the third electrical option and although being a little more specialised than arc, has its applications for the DIY user.

Arc Welding

Arc welders such as the example we chose for this feature, are not particularly complicated pieces of equipment — a fact reflected in that prices start as low as £45. They consist basically of a transformer which can be varied in terms of its output, and which thus determines the 'strength' of the arc being produced. From the welder's casing there appear two leads, one of which is attached to

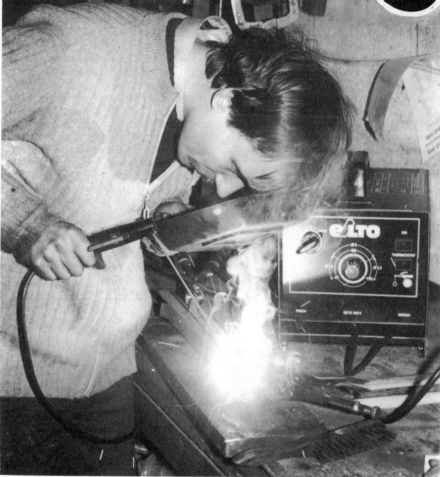

The controls on the average arc welder are usually pretty basic as in this case.

the hand set, and the other which features a large spring clip; this is the earth or return lead (similar to that on a MIG welder). The latter has to be fastened to the work so that a good electrical contact is achieved; therefore it may first be necessary to clean the area where it is to be clamped.

The hand set is an unassuming looking device with a spring loaded lever that controls the jaws at the tip. Into these jaws is placed the electrode which is consumable, and when the current is flowing, produces the electrical arc between itself and the workpiece. This arc develops a very intense but localised heat which rapidly liquifies the metals to be joined and the electrode itself. The electrodes have a central core of steel which is comparable to the parent metal being welded, and are coated in a flux which forms a protective shield as the molten metal is deposited (again similar to that produced by the inert gas in the MIG technique). General purpose electrodes are commonly available and as their name suggests, they can be used for most jobs. However, another limiting fac-

The hand operated lever on the hand set is depressed to open the jaws at the tip, which hold the rod in place.

tor is the current supply which, according to whether it be AC or DC, determines the metal that can be successfully joined. Most of the outfits designed for the home user pro-

Arc, Carbon Arc and Spot welding – Chris Graham reports

The flux coating from the rod is laid down on top of the hot weld and in the ideal case, peels free as it cools . . .

. . . however, if this does not happen, it must be levered or chipped free with the hammer provided – goggles should be worn when attempting this.

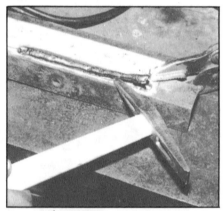

duce an AC current, which means that they are not suitable for welding stainless steel (special rods are required if this is to be attempted). The stop start nature of the AC current is quite suitable for mild steel, but not for the stainless variety, which requires the more stable attention of the DC supply. Aluminium also needs a DC supply. The considerably more expensive rectifier sets have the ability to produce both AC and DC current.

To start the arc welding process you first set up the joint that you require, by clamping it etc. Arc welding is fairly tolerant with regard to dirt on the joint, but flaky rust should be removed. The sensible technician will usually ensure that the area to be joined is as clean as possible, if only for his own peace of mind. If either or both of the metal subjects to be fastened are badly rusted, arc welding should not be attempted. The power of the arc is likely to 'blow' straight through such samples.

Once the earth clamp has been secured the electrode has to be struck against the subject in order to initiate the arc, and this can be likened to the striking of a match. Once this has been tried by the beginner a few times the skill involved will rapidly become apparent. With the open arc produced, the electrode must be maintained at the correct distance from the work to preserve the arc, and at the correct angle (usually about 60 degrees). This

is made difficult enough anyway by having to peer through the dark green eye shield, but when you remember that the electrode is getting shorter all the time and that it is having to be moved along the joint as well, things become quite tricky. Its always a good idea to have plenty of practice on scrap metal as this will hopefully build both your skill and confidence. An easier alternative to the problems outlined above, is provided by the touch or drag electrode. With such rods the arc is maintained by the angle of the rod, and not by the gap. So this means that it can be dragged along the joint to achieve the same end product, but with a lot less trouble.

Arc welding electrodes are available in a number of differing sizes, and these determine the size of the arc which can be produced, and so the thickness of metal that can be welded. One of the biggest advantages of arc welding is the very limited level of distortion which it creates, because the arc is so localised. However, this is not to say that there are no distortions at all, because there are (as the diagrams illustrate), and distortion can be severe on "thinner" parts such as body panels.

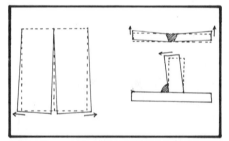

These diagrams (not to scale) illustrate the ways in which different joints distort as they are arc welded.

Generally speaking, arc welding appears to be more suited to work of a heavier nature. It is ideal for use in the fabrication of chassis, axle stands, benches, scaffolding etc. It can be used on car bodywork although the common rod sizes (1.5/1.6mm) take a lot of heat to melt them, which can be too much for the body panel, so to achieve acceptable results calls for practice. The arc welder can be used overhead, downhand (flat on bench) and vertically up or down. Vertical runs obviously create problems as the molten metal tends to

Although thought by many to be rather a basic technique, arc welding can produce some most acceptable results . . .

. . . but care is needed as too much heat can easily 'blow' holes in the subject.

want to drip everywhere. Luckily though there are special rods available for this purpose which help immensely. The other precaution usually taken is that the power is dropped by about 10%, which helps to reduce the 'dribbling' rate.

A further application of arc welding is known as hard facing, where a layer of weld is put down to build a worn surface up in preparation for re-grinding as with a crankshaft for example. The teeth on the buckets of JCB diggers are repaired in such a way as this as it is the most economical way of doing so. So do not despair all you owners of classic JCBs, help is close at hand.

Carbon Arc

Once you own a basic arc welder you immediately open the way to another technique known as carbon arc brazing. This process utilises the heat produced from the arc welder via two consumable carbon electrodes, to heat and melt a brazing rod, and make the joint that way. One of the two electrodes is connected to the power, and the other goes to earth, and therefore an open arc is set up between them. The heat supplied

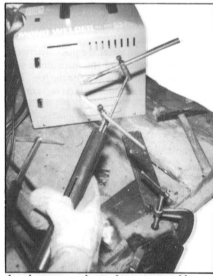

A carbon arc attachment for your arc welder provides a simple and cheap entry into the brazing field. An arc is produced between the two consumable copper coated electrodes which provides the heat for the brazing process – the subject metals are not melted.

should never be sufficient to melt the two metals being joined.

Carbon arc brazing has been described as a clumsy and ungainly technique, and indeed this would seem to be true on first impressions. Dealing with the two consumable rods which come together in a 'V' shape with the arc being produced at the sharp end, is not easy. Older outfits had to be manually operated so that when the rods had burnt too far apart, the brazing had to stop and they had to be re-adjusted by hand to close the gap again. These days however things have been made a little easier because hand sets are now available with controls that enables the rods to be fed in without stopping.

Apart from the initial difficulty of handling the equipment other problems include distortion. This can be quite common with carbon arc work, with one of the contributing factors being that the arc has to be held in one place initially, to warm the metal up and to melt the brazing rod. This gives the heat a chance to spread with sometimes disastrous results. Incidentally, it is possible to cut metal with carbon arc equipment, but this is only with specialised professional equipment that is fitted with a compressed air system to 'blow' through the subject.

Spot welding

Spot or resistance welding relies on a different principle from the common arc in order to make its joint. Electrical resistance provides the heat necessary to fuse the two or more layers of metal together. The spot welder itself is a hand held instrument which is pretty heavy and has two protruding arms. Onto these two arms are fastened the electrodes, which come in many assorted varieties. The body of the spot welder contains a heavy-duty coil together with some other electronic wizardry and sometimes an automatic timer.

The samples of metal are placed between the two electrodes and the machine is activated by depressing the lever on the top. This closes the two electrodes (one on top and the

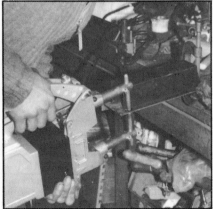

The spot welder, although producing a fine result, is a heavy piece of equipment and so can be a handful to use.

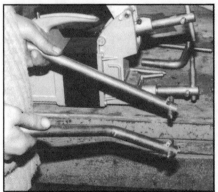

The key to being versatile with a spot welder is to have a large selection of interchangeable electrodes, but these are expensive.

other beneath) onto the metal pinching it tightly together. At the same instant the current begins to flow directly between the electrodes and the resistance which it encounters generates the heat, which melts and fuses the metals together almost instantaneously. The heat produced is very localised and is only applied for a short period, and so distortion is really a thing of the past when you own a spot welder. However, long runs of spot welds can cause problems on thinner subjects so it is best to avoid making such runs by altering your point of attack. Chop and change from one end to the other, the principle involved being akin to tightening a cylinder head.

The electrodes are held tight in the arms by a type of cotter pin fastening. The height of the two electrodes has to be altered in accordance with the thickness of the metal layers being joined.

Preparation is quite important if a lasting weld is to be produced. Basically the relevant areas should be taken back to shiny metal for the best results, and there should certainly be no old paint or rust left to upset the contact. It is also important for the surfaces which are

being joined to be a precise flat fit with each other. Do not simply rely on the pinching action of the welder to achieve this, hand clamps should be used. To be absolutely sure of a tight and slip-free joint, self tapping screws are an excellent idea. They are far less obtrusive than awkward clamps. On the more expensive models a timer is fitted which regulates the duration of the 'power on' stage automatically. This is set in accordance with the thickness of the metal layer under treatment, the relevant information being supplied on a table supplied with the welder. At the cheaper end of the scale I'm afraid it comes down to experience as with no timers fitted on these examples, it has to be judged by the user. Once again practice is a good idea to help gauge the timing, as insufficient heat leads to inadequate fusion and a weak joint, and over enthusiastic heating produces a hole. If holes are created in the workpiece it not only causes problems in that respect, but it also leads to a build up of waste on the electrode. This must not be allowed to occur and to this end special tools are often supplied with the unit for re-shaping the tips.

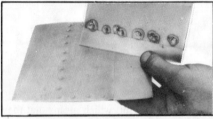

Two examples of spot welding; on the left how it should be done, and, on the right, a beginners attempt. Too much heat is a common failing initially for many newcomers.

Spot welders are perfectly suitable for use on many metals including aluminium and copper but perhaps one of the main disadvantages is the limitation that is created by the shape of the electrodes. To be fully versatile you must carry a large selection of differently shaped arms and these are expensive. Problems are also encountered when fixing new panels to old, unless the original metal is spotless. From a purely practical point of view the newcomer to spot welding will soon discover that overhead work is a real struggle. This is not so much due to a difficulty in technique, but simple to the weight of the unit! Everyone adopts their own favourite 'pose' with the spot welder and this is a matter for personal experimentation — if you'll pardon the expression. Finally a word of warning. Electrical welding does have its dangers, especially from shocks, so use your common sense. Avoid welding under damp or wet conditions, and never complete a circuit between the welder, yourself and the earth clamp! □

> **NEXT MONTH**
> MIG Welding

Metalworking

Part 11

MIG welding — Chris Graham explains this versatile technique.

MIG welding has grown rapidly in popularity over the last few years, in both the professional and the DIY markets — a point well illustrated by the considerable interest shown in our recent 'Migmate' Special Offer. As is the way with most products these days; the technological advances in MIG welding equipment have come thick and fast recently, and have been accompanied by a gradual lowering in the price. This is ultimately good news for the DIY market, and today, as we have shown, kits are available 'over the counter' for just a few hundred pounds.

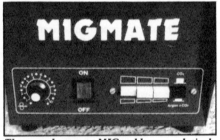

The controls on most MIG welders are relatively simple, with adjustments for the wire speed and heat level, plus an on/off switch and in this case, a gas selector button.

It is all too easy to become totally convinced by the many virtues of MIG welding, once you have tried it. The alternatives open to the metalworker who has no access to MIG equipment are these. Firstly there is gas which, although being very versatile and having many useful applications, is rather slow, bulky and expensive. Secondly there is arc/carbon arc. This seems generally to have earned the reputation (rightly or wrongly) of being rather clumsy and awkward to handle, and so on the face of it, the pendulum starts to swing in favour of MIG. However, to judge for yourself you must appreciate all aspects of the technique, and form your own

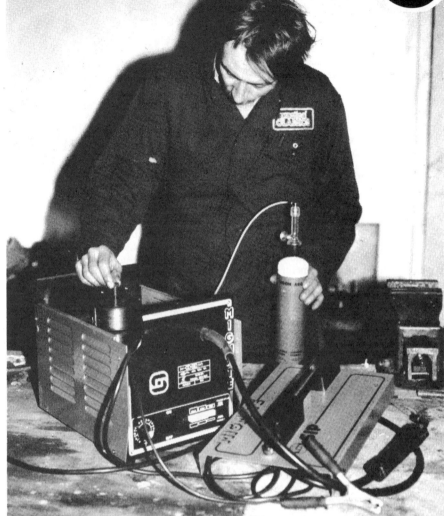

Added to the MIG welding kit of your choice, other tools that will be of use include, a grinder, an assortment of clamps and mole grips, a pair of cutters or pliers and a suitable spatter release spray.

opinion.

The basic principles involved in MIG welding were outlined in our general introduction to the subject published in the October 1985 issue, but I feel they are worthy of another mention here. The actual term 'MIG' is not simply a snappy title thought up by an anonymous 'ad' department somewhere, it actually has a meaning. The letters stand for Metal Inert Gas, which refers to the basis for the success of the whole idea. The age old problem involved with welding has been how to achieve a weld free from porosity and thus weakness. Oxidation which occurs as the weld is laid down, is the main cause of this trouble, and so must be guarded against. In conventional welding the flux fulfils this function but it can be troublesome, and in the case of arc welding, it has to be chipped off the finished weld with a hammer. The flux's job is simply to provide a 'protective' shield around the weld for the time that it is molten, and so vulnerable to oxidation from the oxygen in the atmosphere.

In MIG welding there is no flux, and its place is taken by a specially unreactive gas. This gas is one of a group known as the Inert (or Noble) gases, and it is most commonly argon. In fact, the argon is usually mixed with another gas such as carbon dioxide or nitrogen, and is only present in small proportions (up to 20%). Argon or carbon dioxide are available in separate cylinders but in the main, a mixture of the two is most often chosen for general purpose welding. The gas is supplied from a conventional cylinder to the welder where it is then transferred to the torch. Within the unit there is an electrically operated solenoid which controls the gas flow to the work accurately so that waste is avoided. The solenoid is wired into the main control switch on the hand set.

MIG welding utilises a consumable electrode which is continuously fed to the torch as the welding proceeds, and is supplied from a spool contained within the body of the welder. The power for the wire feed is produced from an electric motor and it too has its control linked to the main switch.

The wire which is tensioned as it leaves the spool, travels into a guide tube which takes it down the main lead to the torch, where it emerges from the nozzle together with the gas, and forms the arc with the subject. The current for the arc is supplied by a transformer that runs from the domestic AC supply, and is similar to that found in an arc welder. Like the gas and the wire feed, the current is also controlled by the single switch on the hand set.

The controls on the front of the MIG welder are usually fairly simple, consisting of a wire speed control, some form of temperature control to provide an adjustment for varying thicknesses of metal, and an on/off switch. Overheating can sometimes occur after continued use and to avoid this, some units are fitted with an automatic cut-out device, or in more expensive models, a fan.

With the smaller MIG welders the gas supply from the cylinder is controlled by a simple valve. A ball bearing indicates the pressure selected.

The wire is fed from its spool, through a spring loaded tensioner, and on into the guide tube which leads it eventually to the nozzle.

Welding with MIG

The basic theory behind MIG welding is the same as that for other types of welding in that the subject metals are fused together by a source of extreme heat. The joint is supplemented by the addition of the welding wire which carries the current to provide the arc and is melted instantaneously. Because all of the functions are controlled from the one switch, the arc does not have to be 'struck' as it does with conventional arc welding. In arc welding actually initiating the arc is quite a haphazard process, as you must be shielded behind the heavily filtered eye protector ready for when it starts, and so cannot see where to start it! However, no such inconveniences exists with MIG equipment, since the nozzle can be visually positioned as closely as required without the risk of an arc being set up (except with the cheapest MIG units, where the nozzle is live and so will arc once it reaches the required distance from the metal). Then it can be held in the desired position while the shield is lowered, and welding

can begin in the right place from the start.

The arc of course completes the circuit and will only 'jump' providing the earth lead is correctly attached. Any problems you have with initiating the arc may well be due to a badly secured earth lead clamp. Old paint can provide a very effective insulator. Also try to avoid positioning the clamp too far away from the area to be welded. In the case of the Migmate that we were using for this feature, the gas supply from the cylinder is controlled by a simple valve, and a ball bearing provides a rough indication of the pressure selected.

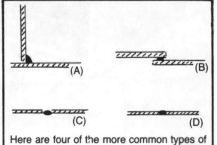

Here are four of the more common types of weld: A – Corner or Fillet weld, B – Lap weld, C – Butt weld, D – Plug weld.

A selection of wire thicknesses are available from your local welding suppliers, but most of the smaller DIY MIG units are capable of handling only the thinner varieties. The common sizes are 0.6mm, 0.8mm, 1.0mm and 1.6mm, with the first two being the most popular for general purpose car work. Steve Demol is of the opinion that 0.6mm wire is the most suitable for car and light sheet metal work, and this is the size that features on the Migmate. The heavier wires will require more heat to work and therefore this will lead to more distortion if they are used on delicate subjects. Steve says that 0.8mm wire will cope adequately with metal varying in thickness from 2mm up to 7mm, however thinner wire can be used on such thicknesses but several 'runs' will be required instead of just one. For specialised work involving the mass production of com-

ponents made from rare alloys etc, custom made welding wire is produced to match exactly the properties of the subject metal. But on a more ordinary level, most people in 'the trade' use a mild steel, copper coated de-oxidised wire. The copper coating and the de-oxidation process help to combat porosity in the final weld.

Armed with all the invaluable knowledge so far stated you may perhaps now feel confident enough to have a go yourself; after all, there is no substitute for experience in techniques such as welding. However, before you rush off and attempt fitting any expensive replacement panels or weld a crucial area of a chassis, it is wise to make some practice runs on a scrap sample first. Really, you should carry on doing this until you acquire the smooth action which is essential for a successful weld. You must be able to maintain the nozzle-to-work distance accurately in order ensure a stable arc, and the speed of travel is important as well. Too slow and the weld will become inconsistant and there will be a risk of blowing holes in the subject, and too fast and the weld will be patchy and lack penetration. Other aspects which you must experiment with yourself are the wire speed and the heat settings. One of the main influencing factors on these two is the subject thickness, but the instruction booklet supplied with your equipment should give some helpful hints on this.

Assuming that your practice sessions have gone well, and you now feel ready to tackle the real job, you should first spare a thought for correct preparation. Although it is not essential for the metals that are to be joined to be spotlessly clean, it does help. If the joint area is brought to a shiny finish with a grinder then the strongest possible weld will result. Such a preparation will ensure the removal of all old paint, underseal, rust, grease and other hinderances, and is certainly recommended. In most cases replacement panels that are purchased already primed need not be cleaned as the arc can usually be 'struck' through the painted layer.

As well as being quick and most effective, MIG equipment is very versatile in the ways it can be used, and because the heat source is

The hand torch features just one button, which controls the current, the gas and the wire feed in one action. The nozzle casing is removable and it is important that this is kept free from blockages.

This is the type of face shield that is supplied with the smaller kits, it has to be hand held which can be a nuisance. The more professional shields are worn on the head leaving both hands free. Ensure that the filter fitted is adequate for the equipment.

so localised, distortion is kept within tolerable limits. Overhead and vertical work is well within the capabilities of the competent user, although adjustments to the equipment will be required first. In such work there is obviously a risk of molten metal dropping from the weld as it progresses, but there are precautions that can be taken. One school of thought recommends that the current be reduced slightly, but Steve has discovered that increasing the wire speed and leaving the current unchanged also has the desired result. An unfortunate effect which Steve terms as 'blobbing' may result if the wire

speed is set too high. In such cases the wire is fed to the weld so quickly that it has no time to be melted, and it repeatedly 'bounces' back off the subject with undesirable results. Trial and error appears once again to be the most satisfactory answer, and Steve suggests that you have a friend standing by to alter the controls in accordance with your instructions during your experiments.

Safety

As usual the safety aspects of this subject cannot be stressed enough. These particularly apply to the inexperienced newcomers who are just learning. One of the biggest dangers in MIG welding is posed by the sparks that are produced. These may look harmless enough but they are quite capable of doing serious damage to the eyes, and burning hands, face and neck. This is why it is so important always to wear gloves, overalls and adequate face protection. Always insist upon genuine cotton overalls as synthetic materials such as nylon burn and melt with horrible results for the skin beneath. A full face shield is always preferable to a pair of goggles, and you must ensure that the green filter is of adequate strength for the purpose. Ordinary gas welding goggles are most definitely not suitable as they are not dark enough and will not provide the necessary protection from the ultra violet rays produced by the arc, The filters provided with the smaller units are safe

The versatility of MIG ensures that it can easily cope with vertical runs. In this case the two sample sheets were tack welded together first, and it is always important to make sure that a close and accurate fit is achieved between the two.

to use with that particular equipment, but be very wary about using them with larger, more powerful welders. You should seek advice before taking any risks which you might regret for the rest of your life. The assistants at your local welding suppliers are the ones to consult about this.

People often wonder about the risks of receiving an electric shock from a MIG welder, and indeed, this can be a very off-putting thought. The noise and the reactions created by the MIG welder in use appear so violent that one tends to assume that the slightest lapse in concentration or minor mistake could lead to some terrible hair-curling shock. But Steve assures me that this is not the case. Short of welding whilst standing in a bucket of water or completing the circuit between the work and the earth clamp, with your own body, the risks of shock are minimal to the conscientious exponent.

With practice results from the MIG can be very presentable. The clumsy looking gloves are essential items in welding, especially for the beginner.

When you are welding under the more unusual circumstances, such as under a car, try to keep yourself out of the way as much as possible. Molten globules down the inside of the shoe, or up the sleeve are the most painful favourites lovingly recounted by experienced welders. These flying globules of molten metal are known collectively as spatter, and have lead to the development of anti-spatter sprays. Such spray should be applied to all surfaces that may be exposed to spatter (the subject, tools and the torch itself) as it will ease the removal of the soldified metal fragments after the welding is finished. □

NEXT MONTH
Types of welded joint and how to make them.

CONTINUED FROM PAGE 41

Metalworking Part 8

question. The regulators need to be checked carefully and you should check for any leaks from the cylinder. Never grease any of the fittings and if any do appear unusually tight, examine them thoroughly for damage. Safety checks can be carried out by appointed specialists; a good idea should you be in any doubt.

The cylinders themselves should be treated with reverence and there are certain golden rules that have to be obeyed. They should always be stored (and used) in an upright position, preferably on a trolly, and should never be exposed to extremes of temperature. The bottle key, which is used to open the main cylinder valves, should always be left with the acetylene cylinder. This is purely a safety measure that will enable the fuel gas to be closed off as quickly as possible in the event of a disaster. A flashback arrester is a useful device that when fitted (between the torch and the cylinder) acts as a safety valve should the gas start burning back towards the cylinder. You must expect to pay about £100 for a pair of flashback arresters. Goggles are of course an essential piece of equipment for gas welding, and to this end should be worn at all times. There are many types now on the market so it is likely that you will find some to suit. Even spectacle

wearers are catered for as one piece goggles with a flip-up green filter section (revealing a clear plastic screen) are now being marketed. Protective gloves are also a wise precaution, although some people find them a bit of a handicap. Controlling the filler wire through a pair of thick gauntlets is not easy, but one remedy sometimes used to overcome this is to cut the tips off of the first two fingers and the thumb of the glove, which makes things a lot easier. Thin leather gloves are available for this purpose, but they are expensive.

Heat dispersion is another point worth mentioning as it really is an unseen enemy. The spread of heat from the torch throughout the surrounding metal is considerable and needs to be borne in mind at all times. This is a major danger when working in the engine compartment with the engine still in place. Obviously it is always best to remove the engine before welding but if this cannot be done, make sure that all fuel pipes have been suitably isolated and be careful with plastic coated wires. If you are repairing sills make sure before you start that the loom does not run down inside the sill. Talking of melting things, if you are welding in the interior of the car, strip out as much as possible before you start. Headlinings, seat covers and carpets are all vulnerable. Always remember not

to swing the flame about when it's alight, for example, when removing goggles, or when turning round to talk to a friend (who should also wear goggles whilst welding is in progress) — a blast from a well tuned welding torch certainly tests the strength of a friendship.

Finally, it is wise to observe the following general safety precautions:
1. Do not weld without a fire extinguisher at the ready.
2. Make sure you have an assistant who will be able to spot fires that you may well miss because of your dark glasses.
3. Do not wear nylon if you can help it.
4. Never rest on a carpet or similar when welding.
5. Remove all flammable material from welding area — paint or stripper tins etc.
6. Fasten clothing at the neck and wrists and wear protective shoes – not sandals.
7. If the car is raised, make sure that it is properly supported.
8. Never allow children or animals into the workshop whilst welding is in progress.

The writer wishes to thank Crawley Welding Supplies Limited (telephone (0293) 29761/2) for the kind loan of equipment for this feature.

CONTINUED FROM PAGE 43

Case hardening

A further heat treatment known as Case Hardening fulfills another useful purpose, but unfortunately will probably be a little beyond the limited resources of the DIY metalworker. Nevertheless, it is perhaps sensible to be aware of this process. As its name suggests, case hardening involves the creation of a hard protective layer around a softer central core. The layer produced is only a matter of a millimetre or so thick and is made from a high carbon steel and so is very tough. This technique is best suited to low carbon steels and works by carburising the surfaces. This means that the surfaces are impregnated by carbon at a high temperature (around 900°C), and this is supplied from substances like charcoal and bone dust or a variety of other chemicals which are rich sources of carbon. One method involves packing the items that are to be case hardened into an iron box and surrounding them with the suitable substance such as charcoal for example. With the box sealed shut it is heated strongly for several hours and then allowed to cool slowly. It is possible to select areas that are not to be coated by covering them with copper or clay, as this will effectively protect them. Probably

Quenching is also a vital process and can be accomplished in a number of mediums including, somewhat surprisingly, air – with the aid of a pressure hose.

the only way that this technique will be of practical use to someone in our position is by the application of a hardening compound. This is specially designed for use on smaller items and conveniently does away with the need for lengthy furnace heating. The sub-

ject is heated to red heat and the compound should then be applied, either by dipping or sprinkling. The job should then be heated still further and finally quenched to complete the process. The hardened layer produced is however, much thinner than that resulting from the commercial technique, and as with all case hardening, the item is likely to need a further hardening and tempering using the methods already outlined earlier.

Finally it is worth mentioning that a gas torch or blow lamp in its own right is a very useful tool to be used on seized nuts and bolts etc., provided that the technique can be applied without any risk of fire. This function relies upon the fact that metal expands slighted when heated, so if the flame is played on the seized nut (but not the stud) it is likely that it will become removable. Similarly, ball and socket joints can often be freed and ball bearings removed from their casings in such a manner. □

NEXT MONTH
Arc, carbon arc, and spot welding.

Metalworking

Part 12

The welded joint is not as simple as you might think — Chris Graham explains, whilst Steve Demol demonstrates.

On the face of it you might assume that welding a joint is a very straightforward process, and provided that enough heat is produced to melt the metal, it will be successful. This is not strictly true however; there are very definite methods and precautions which have to be adhered to in order that the weld be correct and long lasting.

Basically there are four major types of welded joint in common use today and these are: the butt weld, the lap weld, the fillet or corner weld and the edge weld. There are of course variations on these joints and we shall touch on some of these later.

Butt joint

The butt weld is achieved, as its name suggests, when two metal samples are butted together end to end, and welded. As with all types of welding, the preparation for this joint is very important. The two edges that are to be joined must run accurately parallel to each other, so that a tight fit is possible. Welding clamps or mole grips should be used to ensure this close proximity. It is no good at all simply to lay the two pieces down side by side on the bench, and try to weld them that way; this is far too inaccurate.

With the clamps in place the next stage is to tack the joint. The frequency of tacks is determined by the length of the joint and the thickness of metal involved – thicker subjects require less frequent tacking. In cases where the tacks come close together, distortion can be a problem and this must be watched carefully. Any corrections should be made with a hammer after the tacking, and before the final welding. It is important to return the tacked joint to as near perfect as possible. If

Even when welding small items for illustrative purposes, Steve stresses the importance of taking the correct safety precautions. A full and correctly filtered face shield, thick gloves and suitable cotton overalls should all be worn.

The preliminary tacking of a butt weld can lead to distortion if the subject is thin sheet. Any such distortions should be carefully dressed out with a hammer before the final weld is made.

the subjects are thin sheet then the heat produced by the welding run may be sufficient to 'drag' the two halves above the horizontal and distort the final result. One way around this is to gently bend the tacked joint down to just below the horizontal, so that the welding will then pull it back level. The degree to

which it is bent is obviously critical and can only be learned through experience.

Once the tacks have been positioned, it is a good idea to remove all the clamps to enable you to have a clear run at the joint. It is most inconvenient to have to keep stopping to remove each successive clamp. Another tip worth remembering is that it is often a good idea to place a more substantial piece of metal directly under the joint being welded, when the subject is thin sheet. This will help draw off a lot of the heat and so reduce the effects of distortion.

Lap weld

The lap weld is probably the most common weld to be found on the car, or at least, the basic technique is. Most cars are spot welded together for the sake of speed and efficiency, although the lap weld technique provides the basis for this. One sheet is literally 'lapped'

To help reduce the level of distortion when welding a butt joint into a thin subject, it is a good idea to place beneath it a heavier sample of metal. The idea is that the heavier item will take some of the heat straight from the weld, and prevent it from spreading out through the rest of the panel, and causing distortion.

Clamping is vitally important when lap welding. The two edges to be joined must achieve an exact fit together.

over the other (usually by about half an inch), and then they are welded together. Because the spot welder is not a very common piece of equipment in the DIY workshop, a version of lap welding called plug welding can be particularly useful for producing an authentic looking result.

Instead of welding straight down the overlapping joint in the conventional manner, a series of holes is drilled down the edge of the top sheet. Then with the clamps tightly in place, each one is filled with weld. It is best to avoid running straight down the line in succession, but instead to start at one end, then move to the other, then to the middle, and so on. These welds can then be ground smooth and when painted, will take on the appearance of spot welds. Steve says that when filling each hole, he simply runs round the circumference once and this is sufficient to completely fill the hole.

When welding a lap joint in the conventional manner, as in the case of fitting a repair section for example, it is often very helpful to make use of a tool called a joddler. This is basically like a giant pair of pliers which

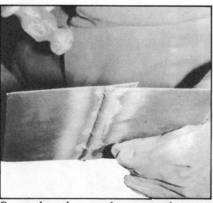

One run down these samples was enough to create this distortion, which illustrates the problem well.

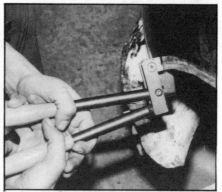

A variation on the lap joint theme involves the use of a joddler. This is particularly useful when fitting a panel repair section as in this case, with the ex-John Williams Jaguar "Mk 1!". The joddler's function is to create a step in the bottom panel so that the repair section can be acurately located, clamped and welded. This type of lap joint leads to a very neat result . . .

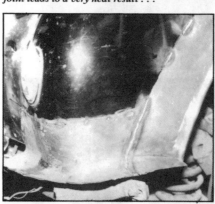

. . . and outwardly it could be mistaken for a butt weld.

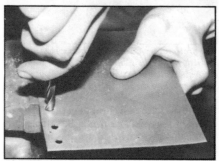

Having drilled the holes in preparation for plug welding, they must be de-burred with a large drill (but keep the gloves on — drills can cut fingers!).

As you might have guessed, clamping is also essential for plug welding. Steve adopts a circular motion to 'fill' each hole . . .

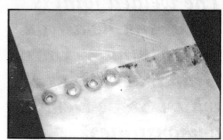

. . . and the results are impressively neat. On the right a few seconds with the grinder has disguised the plugs almost completely.

The edge weld, like the others, is tacked first to secure it. Doing this requires a steady hand as the tacks must be put directly on the edge . . .

. . . as must the final weld. When this is cleaned up it produces a very tidy and distortion free joint.

instead of simply squeezing, moulds the metal to produce a small step. This is used on the bottom panel to enable the top one to sit neatly into it. The weld can then be run around the edge of the step once it has been tacked, and then ground off flush with the level of the panel, to produce an 'invisible' join — sounds simple doesn't it! Once the tacking has been completed check carefully

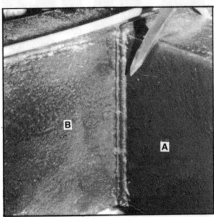

This area of the Land-Rover chassis provides an excellent example of a fillet weld. The outrigger (A) is welded to the main chassis rail (B) where it touches.

sonal preference. He finds it a lot easier with the MIG or the Arc.

With this method tacking is important and distortion can be a problem. When for example, you are fixing a tube to a base, make sure that the tacks are evenly spaced around the circumference. Shrinkage is also a problem, especially when welding single plate. As the newly welded joint cools it can shrink and pull the component towards the weld, so once again, calculated bending at the tacking stage may be advisable. In some cases the situation may arise where a much thinner gauge of metal is being welded onto a thicker sample. Under these circumstances care is needed to avoid distortion in the thinner piece. The one precaution that can be taken against this is to play the heat on to the heavier metal as much as possible.

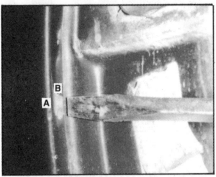

An obvious example of a lap weld on the Spitfire is provided by the joint between the 'B' post (B) and the rear wing (A).

on all lap joints, that the two layers have not separated due to the heat. Any such gaps will be hard to bridge with weld, and will probably result in an untidy finish. Another useful tip to remember is that it is sensible to grind off the tack welds before making the final run, especially when using electric welding equipment. The reason for this is that the tacks are likely to provide that little bit of extra resistance which will prevent complete weld penetration of the metal thicknesss. When using gas this is not such a serious problem as you have the flexibility to play the heat on the tacks for a few seconds longer each time, which will be sufficient to do the trick.

Fillet weld

The fillet or corner weld occurs when the end of one sheet comes in contact with the side of another, and is welded there. Another example is provided when a tube is fixed to a flat sheet by welding around its base. Fillet joints are encountered on cars in areas such as the chassis and the sills. Steve recommends that such welds be done with electrical equipment rather than with gas, but this is only his per-

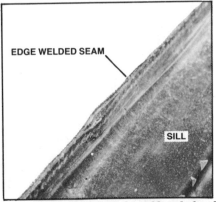

A common example of an edge weld can be found on cars where replacement sills have been fitted, like our Spitfire for example. In this case there are three separate layers of metal that have been edge welded together.

Edge weld

The edge weld is the last type that we shall be considering here. It is achieved when two sheets, both with returns, are butted together so that these returns meet, and they are welded along this inside edge – hence the name. The returns on the panels are normally set at 90 degrees, and they provide a very

good method of joining the sheets. This method is virtually distortion free as the heat is effectively prevented from running through the rest of the panel by the returns. A typical example of this type of weld can be encountered when fitting replacement sills. With edge welding clamping is vital as a perfect fit must be achieved down the whole length. Steve would advise that if you own or have access to gas equipment, use it for this type of welding. Often, he says, you can get away without needing to use any filler wire, as the joint can simply be fused together as it stands. This of course does depend upon the accuracy of the fit between the two returns, so it is well worth spending a lot of time dressing out any imperfections. If everything goes correctly, a very neat join should result and there will be no grinding required.

For all of these types of welding a sensible and methodical approach to the preparation is a very good idea. All the hints and tips concerning this and the important safety aspects which we have pointed out in earlier episodes in this series, should be taken note of before any work begins. □

NEXT MONTH
Welding box sections and
bending pipes.

Metalworking

Part 13

Chris Graham reports on bending metal pipe and sheet.

Pipe benders are no problem to hire these days and they are supplied with all the accessories needed. The diameter of the pipe that can be bent on any one machine is limited by the size of the 'former' supplied with it. It is perhaps a good idea to take a sample of pipe with you to the hire shop to make sure. Some pipe benders are floor mounted (ie, with a stand) and others, like this one have to be secured in a vice. A hire charge of £8 per day is a typical price for such a tool.

Of these two processes, the bending of metal sheet is perhaps the more useful to the DIY car restorer. The ability to form box sections can be a valuable asset if you are engaged in the resurrection of an elderly chassis, for example. Pipe bending, on the other hand, is much more of a specialised affair. Its applications are fairly limited in the motoring field, however, most DIY people have to call upon the techniques involved at some stage during their motoring lives.

Because both of these techniques are only used on rare occasions by the amateur, he will find that in most cases it will not be worth his while to purchase the equipment. This leaves the obvious alternative of hiring the tools, which usually provides a very satisfactory solution. Hire shops are as common as McDonalds these days so there should be few problems on this score. Prices should normally be reasonably affordable on a day rate basis and the equipment is, on the whole, well maintained.

Cutting your length of pipe with a hack saw is the most obvious method and if you are right handed, it is best to cut on the right hand side of the vice. This is a simple precaution against rapping your knuckles.

Pipe bending

Most type of pipe (aluminium, steel, copper etc) can be bent to good effect, however there are problems. Perhaps some people imagine that bending can simply be done over the edge of the bench, or even across the knee but this is not the case. The act of bending a tube causes the metal on the outside of the curve to be stretched, and that on the inside to be 'shrunk'. The stresses that this creates within the sample are quite sufficient to cause considerable distortion if correct support is not given, and this is where the pipe bender earns its money. Bending a sample of light tubing across the bench edge will have disastrous results on the 'roundness' of the tube at the point of the bend. If you imagine what happens to a paper straw when a bending force is applied to it, then you will get some idea of how the equivalent sample in metal will react.

To prevent this collapse the pipe bender supports the sample on both sides as the bend is made, and so the forces are kept even. The other major problem involved with this technique is the positioning of the curve. A fair degree of level headed planning will be necessary to ensure that the sample ends up as you originally intended, especially if more than one curve is to be made. It is always wise to use a slightly longer than necessary length of pipe so that any indiscretions may be allowed for.

This 'puckering' around the bend area is obviously a real headache if you do not have access to a proper pipe bender, but there are ways around it. If you have no alternative but to make the bend in any way you can, you should first fill the pipe with some form of ballast. This will in effect, make it 'solid', and so prevent any major distortion. Ordinary substances such as earth or sand can be used for this packing process, but the important thing is to get it filled fully, and tightly. Use a bung or cork to ensure that the contents of the pipe remain tightly packed during bending. Lead provides an alterative to sand or soil but obviously has to be heated which can be troublesome to the small operator. However, the most convenient method involves the use of a substance called Cerrabend. This is a commercially produced compound that looks just like ordinary solder, but the difference is that it melts at the boiling point of water. This makes it easy and relatively safe to handle but the one drawback is the price — it is expensive.

Next the runner must be inserted and the stop (arrowed) brought to bear on the end of the pipe. This is hooked over to anchor the pipe and enable the bending to take place.

Producing a twist free section that involves more than one curve can be tricky, so it is sensible to take the precaution of using a small spirit level. The first bend is made and then can be used as a base from which to check the level for the second.

This device is called a pipe cutter so its function is self-explanatory. It is particularly useful when cutting small diameter copper pipe since a normal hacksaw would be too clumsy. A small cutting wheel is rotated and simultaneously wound in to cut the pipe, and this ensured that a very accurate edge is produced. The pipe cutter can also be used simply for marking. This is particularly applicable on large diameter samples that are to be cut with a saw. The line produced helps make a straight saw cut possible which leads to a much more workable result. When cutting large tube it is wise to cut through the top thickness, and then to rotate it and make the next cut, and so on.

The bend is then made with a slow and deliberate pressure.

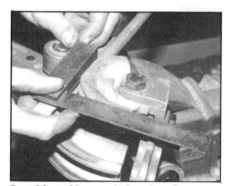

One of the problems can be knowing when to stop, so some form of pattern is a good idea. If it is right angled bend that you want, then a set square is the answer. Always be cautious as you near the completion of the bend as it can be hard to correct an over-bent sample.

Often you will find that fine adjustments are required before the perfect result is achieved. A good way of making these involves a length of larger diameter pipe and a vice. The pipe is slipped over the end of the sample, which in turn secured in a vice at the appropriate angle. Care is needed to avoid damaging the pipe in the vice and soft jaws are recommended to reduce this risk.

Marking is an important stage as without it, inaccuracies can creep in. The start of the proposed bend should be marked and then lined up against the end of the former.

Solid bars can also be bent using a pipe bender and this is useful in the production of U bolts for example. However, mild steel, brass and copper should be heated to a cherry red (about 750-800 degrees C) and although the brass and copper can be cooled before being bent the steel must be red hot, which will almost certainly damage metal benders with soft alloy formers. A home-made bender may solve this problem (see page **56**).

Copper brake pipes are often replaced by the DIY restorer and due to their size and softness, they can be bent like this. Care is still needed though and all movements should be gradual and controlled.

For those with a bit of money to spend (£10 plus), various tool manufacturers produce small pipe benders for this very purpose . . .

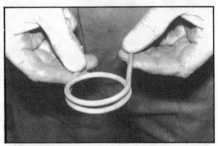

. . . they are easy to use and provide a perfect bend. Even 'pig tale' coils are simple to produce with a bit of practice. Metal fuel lines are another application for hand pipe benders.

Sheet benders, like pipe benders, are available in a number of sizes, and this determines the width of sheet that can be catered for. Some, like this one, are designed to be gripped in a vice or welded to a convenient bench end. Others are supplied with legs. This one could easily cope with anything up to about 16 gauge sheet.

A box section such as this can be made in a matter of minutes, even by the beginner. Such structures can be particularly useful when chassis repairs are required. Steve advises that nothing thicker than 16 gauge be used for chassis work.

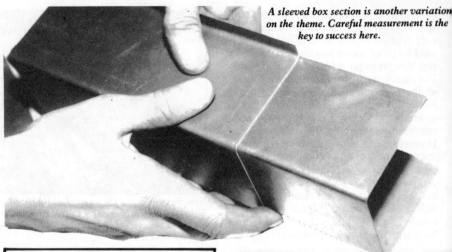

A sleeved box section is another variation on the theme. Careful measurement is the key to success here.

Working out the cutting size

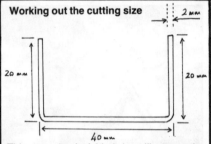

This example of a folded sheet illustrates the bend allowances that must be taken into consideration when initially measuring out the metal. This drawing has been made to the *external* dimensions of the section, and takes into account the metal thickness. To produce this example from a flat sheet the total cutting size must be calculated, and this is dome as follows:

$$(40—4) + (20—2) + (20—2)$$
$$= 36 + 18 + 18$$
$$= \textbf{72mm}$$

In other words, each right-angle bend reduces the length of cut sheet required by twice its thickness, and the size of the cut sheet prior to bending will equal the total of the *internal* dimensions in this example.

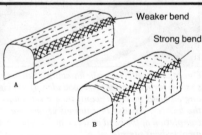

As a result of the rolling methods used to produce sheet metal, a grain structure a little similar to that which exists in wood, is created. This runs down the length of the strip and has an effect on its structural properties. This diagram shows how running with or against the grain can effect the strength of a proposed bend. If the bend is made 'with' the grain as in example A, there will be a tendency for it to crack in time. Therefore, it is better to make the bend as in example B, especially when thick sheet is involved.

A DIY bar bender

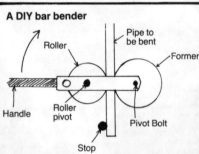

This type of set-up can easily be made by the amateur and used for bending solid bar (for U bolts etc). The pivot bolt should be welded on to a base plate and then a selection of varying formers can be made from scrap bar and the like, and drilled to fit. The stop should also be welded to the base. The roller should not be made too small as this will hinder its ease of movement, and the handle should be made long enough to provide sufficient leverage.

The bending of sheet metal on the other hand, is a much simpler process. It does not involve nearly so much method and there are not the same problems to tackle. The secret of producing an accurate box section is in the measuring out. Using the bender itself should pose few problems as it is very straightforward. The crucial factor to remember is that the metal sheet does have a thickness, and that although this may be a matter of millimeters, it is nevertheless not to be overlooked. In most cases box sections have to be made to fairly exact dimensions, and these can go drastically astray if the thickness of the sheet is not taken into consideration. The diagram shown here illustrates how these dimensions should be used to work out the cutting size of sheet required. □

NEXT MONTH
Repairing aluminium & cast iron castings.

Metalworking

Part 14

Got a broken or cracked alloy casting? Chris Graham looks into some repair methods

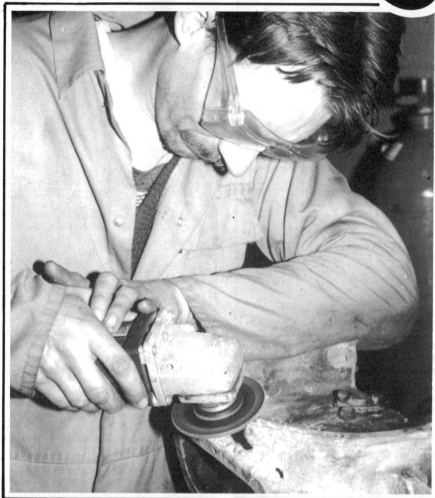

The technique of casting has been around for a long while, many hundreds of years in fact, and over this time the principles involved have remained much the same. Of course there are alternatives to casting as a method of component production but these do not compare very favourably on practical grounds, in today's economic climate. Both forming the item from a solid block of metal or making it up from accurately shaped

Large castings such as this Austin 7 crankcase with its shattered clutch housing are well within the bounds of practical repair. However, the secret is knowing exactly what it is made of so that the correct welding rods can be chosen – without them the job is virtually impossible.

pieces are ludicrously expensive and time consuming in comparison.

Casting involves producing the desired item from a mould that is made using special sand. A 'pattern' which accurately represents the component (usually made from varnished wood) is sunk into the sand which is then packed tightly around it. The pattern can then be removed to leave a perfect impression which is filled with molten metal. This is allowed to solidify and the casting is made. However, sacrifices are made for the sake of speed and efficiency and the result is that castings are brittle and will not generally withstand shock or impact of any kind, and they are also prone to cracking if exposed to sudden changes in temperature, so damage of one sort or another is fairly common. When this does occur the repair can be made by arc welding, gas welding, MIG or TIG welding or brazing. Iron is often used for casting but in general, it is more troublesome to repair. For a start it can be expensive. If arc welding is your chosen method, a packet of suitable rods is likely to cost about £60. Gas and TIG

Preparing the area properly is important. Any loose or cracked segments should be removed (with a hammer if necessary) and then the edge ground to a fairly smooth and clean finish.

can be used as alternative methods as can brazing (using a silicon/bronze rod), but some iron castings simply cannot be welded. One of the hardest tasks is identifying the type of castings you have. If you are in any doubt about this, it is probably advisable to seek knowledgable opinion elsewhere on the matter. A further problem is caused by the

Having prepared the area the next stage is to pre-heat it. In this instance we used a gas welding torch but a household blow lamp should be just as effective. Note how the match is being used to 'test' the temperature. Unfortunately though we did not get much further with this example as Steve found it impossible to lay down the first run onto which the rest of the repair could be built. The casting seemed to contain sand and other impurities which prevented a weld being made.

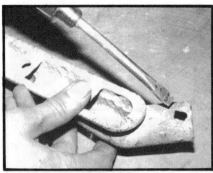

The damage to this cast aluminium water manifold is typical of that found on elderly castings (it too is from an Austin 7). The casting as a whole had taken on a light matt grey appearance which pointed to an oxide build-up – similar to an anodised component. The metal around the hole was wafer thin and it was crumbly, which made it very hard to repair with weld. The only alternative would have been to sleeve it and make it good that way.

This manifold on the other hand (off a 'modern' Alpine I hasten to add) proved to be much more of a repairable item, and to begin with the edges of the hole were cleaned...

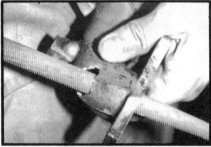

...using a variety of different files...

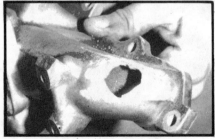

...to produce a finish ready for welding.

fact that the iron has to be heated considerably before welding can begin, and this is usually beyond the ability of the DIY blow lamp.

One of the most commonly used metals in the construction of castings is aluminium and this poses ists own problems when repairs are required, which are due to the metal's ability to conduct heat so readilly. This property causes the localised that is supplied by the welding torch to spread rapidly throughout

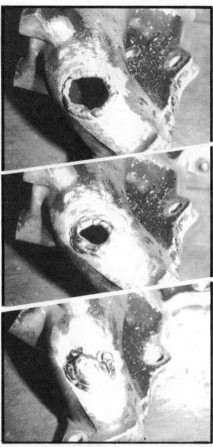

One of the approved methods of making such a repair involves working the weld round and round spiralling inwards towards the centre, as this sequence shows.
The torch can be used to smooth out the finished weld to some degree. Careful application in a similar circular motion can improve the result no end. Remember that the finished weld must not be quenched in any way for fear of cracking the casting.

the whole casting, making actually reaching the correct welding temperature difficult. The answer of course is to pre-heat the area. On the motorcar some typical examples of castings are the cylinder head, the block and the bell housing, and with large items such as these, a lot of pre-heating is required. Smaller articles such as the thermostat housing will obviously require less heating, and in some cases, none at all.

In the case of the damaged aluminium casting, the area should be heated to about 450°C, and there are certain guides that can be used to indicate roughly when this temperature has been reached. One method involves dragging a match (not the striking end) across the heated area and observing whether or not it leaves a black carbon trail. A similar test can be performed with a piece of soap. The crucial thing however, is to avoid over-heating the sample as it is easy to melt it. In most cases the DIY type gas flame gun should be enough, but a gas welding torch may need to be called upon. You should also remember to heat gradually, bearing in mind how easily castings can be cracked.

Obviously the degree of damage to be repaired can vary from a few cracks to a gap-

ing hole, but there are techniques for dealing with most eventualities. The problem is in deciding by which method you are going to effect the repair, though in most cases this decision will be made for you by the equipment that you have available. Aluminium has to be welded using DC equipment when using Arc equipment and such sets are far from common amongst the DIY owners.

The reason for this is a rather technical one, but is basically due to the 'stop/start' nature of the AC current (as opposed to the 'continuous flow' of the DC), which creates a heating and cooling (and cleaning) effect. When using DC equipment, the 'cleaning' action is provided by the flux coated rods, and this is essential to prevent oxidation. As a general rule, magnetic metals (those containing iron) can be welded with AC equipment, but the non-magnetic ones require a DC supply. Gas equipment is a more readily available but slow alternative and does require the addition of aluminium welding flux and suitable rods. The choice of rods is of major importance as the wrong one simply will not weld.

Both MIG and TIG (Tungsten Inert Gas) are particularly useful if large holes are to be filled as they are both fast and do a good job but TIG is the best as it combines great flexibility with speed to produce a very clean result.

However, if the method you have chosen requires the use of welding rods, you must decide positively which type you need, and the first step in this choice is to determine exactly what metal or metal alloy you are dealing with. Each variation will require a welding rod of different metal 'make up' – there is a large selection available on the market. It is a good idea to talk to someone 'in the trade' about what types of rods they use for different jobs, or failing that, to find out from the original manufacturers what, exactly, the casting is made of. Then you can take this information to your local welding suppliers and they should be able to advise you from there.

A pure aluminium casting will usually require an aluminium/silicon rod (with 5% or 10% silicon) to weld it successfully, but if the aluminium has been anodised the rod will probably need to be either pure aluminium or an aluminium/magnesium alloy (5% magnesium). Anodising is a process whereby the aluminium casting is coated in a layer of oxide film (a few microns thick) using an electrolytic process. This greatly increases its resistance to corrosion but has a detrimental effect upon its affinity to the welding torch. In fact such a coating has to be removed before welding can begin, and a grinder is required for this. The coating is very tough and it will require a lot of effort to remove it.

Preparation

Regardless of the technique being used, the preparation before welding begins is very important. As we have discoverd in previous welding articles, the ultimate success of the weld depends on whether or not you have clean metal on which to work. This is obviously not such a problem on aluminium castings as they do not rust, but oxides and dirt can accumulate and need to be removed. Angle grinders, rotary files, hand files and chisels are all useful tools to have handy at this stage, and it is also a good idea to splash on some de-greasing solution as well.

If the repair that you have undertaken involves the 'sticking back together' of a broken component, you may discover further faults along the broken edge during the cleaning stage. Blow holes which are like small air bubbles within the casting can become apparent, and if you do not grind these out, you should at least make sure that they are clean. In some castings (especially older ones) you will find sand within the metal and these will have originated from the sand packing at the actual casting stage. Close inspection will be needed to detect this

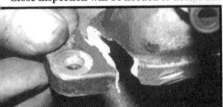

This broken mounting lug provided another fairly typical need for a repair. Some people might imagine that as the two pieces are an exact fit with each other as they stand, that this is how they should be welded back together, but this is not the case.

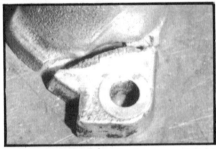

Both edges should be filed back to a smooth finish and slightly 'Veed' (the top of the crack made slightly wider than the bottom. This will help the weld to penetrate to the base of the joint easily, thus ensuring an even weld. In this case setting the two up for welding was easy – a flat surface was quite adequate.

fault but it is worth the effort. If they are left in place during welding they will rise up to the surface as the metal becomes molten, to cause all sorts of problems. They should be ground back to 'clean' metal as soon as they are spotted. The main objective at this stage is to produce a clean and smooth edge but at the same time, retaining its basic shape. *If you use a grinding wheel to clean up an aluminium casting never use that same wheel on steel subjects – it could explode as the aluminium fragments clog the wheel and cause it to overheat.*

In cases where there is a crack to be welded up it should be drilled at each end to halt it

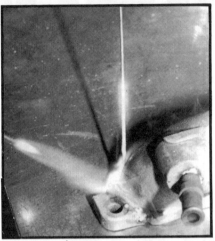

Keep the welding rod well coated in flux at all times.

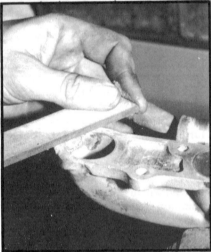

With some careful filing...

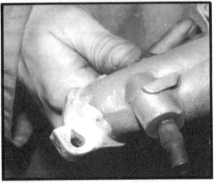

...an invisible joint can be the happy result.

and then gouged out slightly. The holes should be plugged with weld and their size varied according to the casting thickness – thicker casting, larger hole. The gouging is necessary in order to widen the crack out so that its base can be reached by the weld. It's no good for example, simply running the weld along the top of the crack and not allowing it to penetrate to the base, as this will not stop the crack from continuing its downward progress. However, all cracks are not as sim-

ple to locate and repair – some are not even visible to begin with. A casting may well be leaking through invisible cracks and to detect these a special dye system is required. A coloured dye penetrant is sprayed on to one side of the casting over the area that is thought to be damaged. Then a dye developer is added to the same side, and on the reverse side the results can be watched for. With time, the dye should percolate through and become visible thus locating the cracks exactly.

Heat problems and finishing

As I have mentioned already, the casting is not at all happy when subjected to sudden extremes in temperature, and this fact can cause problems at both the welding and the cooling stages. Cracking while you weld is a distinct problem and can be very discouraging – welding one crack well only to find that you have created half a dozen others! A lot of the problem here is caused by the 'on/off' effect of the welding process, but one way around this is to try and keep the sample uniformly hot throughout the welding period. This is best done with the aid of a friend with another gas torch, which he continually plays on the area to reduce the temperature fluctuations.

Cooling the casting after welding is the other problem and often people make very elementary errors. Never quench the casting in any solution or use an air line to cool it. Rapid methods of cooling such as these spell disaster as fresh cracks will inevitably result. Even a cool draught in the workshop can be enough to cause damage. It is essential that cooling is done in a controlled and gradual manner. Gas flames can be used to slow down the cooling rate but this is a time consuming and laborious method. Sometimes heavy metal boxes are used to provide a controlled atmosphere for the casting, but probably not many of us have large, heavy metal boxes in the workshop so this is of little help. A sand filled container can be used to good effect, but one of the most practical ways of ensuring crack-free cooling is by using the oven of an ordinary electric or gas cooker. This idea may encounter considerable resistance from certain members of the household, but if you can swing it, it's a very good method.

In the case of casting repairs, finishing is largely a matter of what is required by each individual job. If you can possibly do so, it is a good idea to leave the repair 'as welded', and not to do any grinding back at all. The reason for this is that there will again be a risk of cracking when using the grinder. However, if for cosmetic reasons the weld must be finished off to a smooth and undetectable finish, then care will be needed. ☐

NEXT MONTH
Metalworking tools and equipment.

Metalworking

Part 15

Chris Graham and Steve Demol survey some of the more unusual tools for the DIY workshop.

The tools for this feature were all supplied thanks to the kind assistance of Alexon Tools (135 Station Road, Beeston, Nottingham, NG9 2AZ, telephone 0602-221041), and represent only a fraction of their vast stock.

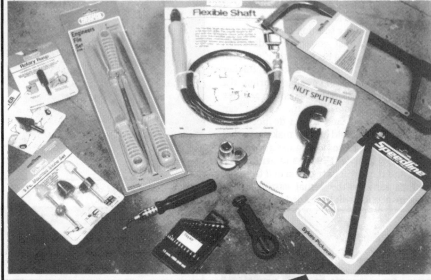

The stud extractor/setter tool is one of those pieces of equipment that is invaluable when it is needed, but will just sit on the shelf for the rest of the time. This particular design from Draper is very simple in its operation, with an offset knurled wheel being pressured against the offending stud. The power is supplied from a ½" socket drive.

The one factor which limits the size of stud that can be tackled, is the size of the hole. The tool is very sturdy and the beauty of it is that there is nothing to go wrong. Price £12.99.

For this penultimate episode in our metalworking series we have decided to return to basics, and look further at the tools of the trade. However, we shall not be considering equipment such as hammers, screwdrivers, spanners and the like, but instead will investigate a few of the less common items which are equally useful.

The selection that we have chosen also includes files, drills and a hack saw which on the face of it, don't seem like unusual tools, but they often get neglected in such features, so we felt that they deserve a mention here.

A thread file could be considered an essential for any car restorer's tool box — we certainly could have used one extensively on the Land-Rover project recently. It consists of a length of square section metal with a hand grip in the middle. At each end there are the teeth, and these differ on each of the eight faces and represent the common thread sizes. External and internal versions are available and it is probably useful to have a thread gauge handy as well, to save on the trial and error method of determining the size of file for the particular thread. The use of thread gauges was outlined in the Taps and Dies feature in the April 1985 issue. One word of warning is that you should never drop a thread file, they are very brittle and so break easily. Price £5.30.

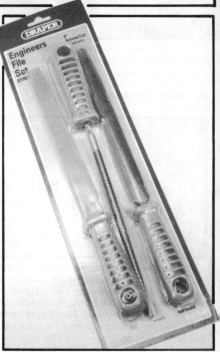

Everyone should be equipped with a set of files, and this offering from Draper provides a very good starting point. Steve thinks that added to these, you would need a rasp such as a Surform, and a selection of needle files, and this would be enough to see you through most eventualities. These new Draper files are fitted with plastic handles that are not detachable, however, the older versions are not. Secondhand files can often be purchased without handles, or with loose wooden ones. Never use a file without its handle as you could slip and impale your wrist on the 'tang' (the sharp metal support for the handle). Steve suggests that if the handles are loose you can secure them by heating the tang to a dull red heat, and pressing it firmly into the handle. Price £9.99.

The rotary rasp could be considered a slightly crude tool, but is, nevertheless, useful. They are particularly suited to enlarging holes rapidly, although you should take care with their application. If for example, they are used on material that is too hard, or they are run at too slow a speed, then there is a risk that the teeth will be stripped out. They are produced with a variety of tooth sizes, and the one shown here (fairly coarse) is ideal for the softer metals such as copper, brass and aluminium. The 'softer' rasps can be used on harder metals. Price £1.99.

Drills deserve a mention here if only to warn you not to buy the cheapest available. A decent set like this one from Napier, will be made from High Speed Steel, and will have been properly hardened for the longest possible life between sharpenings. It is most definitely worth paying that little bit extra to ensure quality. Price £6.29.

Large drills of high quality are expensive and a cheaper alternative is a hole cutter like this one made by Taylor Tools. However, as with all cheap alternatives, the hole cutter has its disadvantages. The biggest snag with it is the constant danger of accidentally making the hole too large. Because it is a conically shaped drill it is easy to go too far, so Steve advises that you mark the maximum diameter of the hole required, and work to that line. The hole cutter does require a pilot hole to be drilled first. One point that Steve did make concerning the use of this tool was, that it requires a variable speed drill. This is because as the hole gets progressively larger, the drill speed should be reduced. Steve considers it an ideal implement for making rough holes for aerial or bumper fitment, where a rubber grommet can be used to hide any small inaccuracies. Price £3.99.

Having drilled your new hole, the next problem is de-burring. This can often result in laborious filing which is made tricky if the access is limited, but if you own a de-burring tool, your troubles are over. This Spiralux example impressed Steve greatly, it was easy to use and very effective. A conventional screwdriver type handle leads to a specially shaped blade that is allowed to swivel in its mount. This is run around the burred edge of the hole, and within seconds the sharp edges are removed. The treatment should be applied to both sides of the hole. The tool is also useful along straight edges. Price £5.75.

Nuts which are well and truly rusted onto their studs are a common problem encountered by restorers, and everyone seems to have their own favourite way of dealing with them. Heat, hack saws, chisels and brute force and ignorance are usually high on the list of most popular methods, but have you ever thought of a nut splitter. I know it sounds painful, but it really isn't, and there is no damage done to the thread either. The Speed-line model that we tried here features a type of G clamp design, and was most effective. The clamp is placed around the offending nut and tightened using suitable means. The sharp 'cutting' edge is forced into the nut as you tighten, which then begins to distort. This then loosens it enough so that it can be removed. Remember not to break through the nut or you will damage the thread. This model is designed for large nuts, but there are other more lightweight versions available. Space can be a problem when using these. Price £7.10.

There are two golden rules to be observed concerning hack saws and the first one is to ensure that the blade is fitted the right way round. The teeth should be angled forward so that they cut on the forward stroke. The second rule is that the blade should always be slackened off when the saw is not in use as this helps prevent the lugs, which support it, from distorting. It is important to select the correct blade for the material being cut, for example, thin sheet needs a fine blade. The blades are measured in TPI which stands for teeth per inch. The hack saw illustrated here is made by Draper and can take either 10" or 12" blades as it has an adjustable frame. Price £7.99.

Another useful attachment for your electric drill is the Taylortools Flexible Shaft shown here. The shaft fastens to the drill via a spindle at one end, and has a conventional chuck at the other. This enables you to add whichever attachment you need and so makes it a usefully versatile tool. Here it is fitted with a mounted stone grinding attachment which provides an ideal way for cleaning and blending welds that have been made in awkward positions. It can be used for general cleaning too with a wire brush fitted. Drilling is another obvious application. Price £13.99.

Safety

As we are always stressing in *Practical Classics*, safety should always be one of your highest priorities whenever you are in the workshop. The accidents always occur during those little jobs where you thought there was no danger. Any task that involves the use of an electric drill should be accompanied by the wearing of safety goggles — this cannot be stressed enough. It only takes one flying fragment during an unguarded moment to cause serious eye damage, if not blindness. Gloves are advisable as a precaution but many people find them more of a nuisance than a help. Take care also to watch for any loose clothing or hair getting caught in the machinery. □

The Spannerman Tool Club is an organisation run by Alexon Tools and provides, for a modest membership fee, access to their extensive catalogue (over 4000 items). The tools supplied are all popular brand names and are guaranteed and available at the club discount. All prices quoted here are from their catalogue. My thanks go to Mr J. Dumelow of Alexon Tools for his help with this feature.

Metalworking

Part 16

Chris Graham looks at some air and electrical tools, and their uses

We gathered together a selection of compresors, spray guns and accessory kits for evaluation. The aim was to approach them from the raw beginner's point of view, using only the instructions provided for guidance.

Compressed air is a remarkably useful commodity to have on hand in the workshop. It can present a practical challenger to electricity as a power source if available with sufficient volume and pressure, but achieving this can be a stumbling block for the DIY restorer. Large and expensive compressors are required to produce continuous high pressure, and these are, quite frankly, beyond the means of most amateurs. Therefore, such people have to settle for smaller units with correspondingly smaller outputs, which does tend to limit the uses to which they can be put. But exactly what are these uses, and how do they compare with what is available from the electrical tool range?

Actually setting up the compressors for the first time was not as simple as you might believe. To be honest, we found the instructions very vague and lacking in confidence-building practical information. I felt that they tended to suffer as a result of the translations, and that a much more detailed step by step approach should have been adopted. To be fair, however, it must be said that Kestrel are in the process of producing a much more useful instruction booklet that will soon be supplied with their units. The compressor shown here provides a typical example of a 50 litre tank (Kestrel C50/200D) and will cost somewhere in the region of £340. (We did not fit its handle and wheels for our trial.)

You only need to glance through a suitable catalogue to discover the vast range of both air and electrical tools now available – the choice is truly impressive. But more often than not with the professional equipment, the price is impressive too, and this is the limiting factor for most people. The lesson to learn appears to be to make your choices carefully, especially where compressors are concerned. Once you have chosen, however, the attachments are not nearly so much of a problem. Each unit has its own range of accessories that are 'dedicated' to it, and most importantly of all, match its individual power output accurately.

The output of a compressor is gauged in

The controls of the C50/200D are clear and easy to manage. The larger gauge indicates the pressure within the tank, and the smaller one shows the output pressure chosen. This is important and is controlled by the plastic knob above it. The output pressure must be matched accurately to the limitations of the accessory being used. But none of this is explained in the instructions! The black knob on top of the large black box turns the compressor on and off. You should always use this control for switching off, never turn the unit off straight from the mains. Using the correct switch evacuates the cylinder, and prevents the motor having to start under a load next time it is switched on.

two ways; the first is the maximum pressure at which it will work, which is measured in pounds per square inch (psi), and the second is cubic feet per minute (cfm). The cfm rating of the compressor represents the maximum volume of air that it is able to produce, and which is available for use by any chosen attachment. However, the cfm figure is a theoretical calculation and differs from the actual free air delivery (FAD) of the unit. The FAD figure is the really important one as it represents the true amount of air that is produced at the end of the hose – which is where it really matters. The FAD value can often be 15-20% down on the stated cfm rating for the compressor, so it is worth asking

The type and size of compressor that is likely to fall within the budget of the DIY enthusiast does have its limitations, but kits of attachments such as this one from Clarke provide a range of equipment that represents most of the tasks that can usefully be tackled. This particular kit is made to professional specifications and is available at a retail price of £59.

about this when buying. The accessories are rated according to their air consumption, and this is again represented as a cfm figure which makes the two easy to compare. It is obviously pointless to try and run a tool with a 15cfm rating on a 6cfm compressor, and this is an important factor that must be remembered, especially when buying secondhand tools.

It is an unfortunate fact that the compressors which are of an affordable price for the DIY restorer are not man enough to cope with the really useful air tools such as ½" impact wrenches, orbital sanders and polishers and angle grinders. But on the other hand, this is just as well for the manufacturers of the equivalent electrical tools, as it allows them a slice in the lucrative DIY market. The business of choosing your electric equipment is simple by comparison, as provided you have a 240V supply and an adequate extension lead, you can buy anything. The one thing to watch for is that you do not mistakenly purchase a three-phase tool, which is not suitable for the domestic 240V supply.

Tyre inflation is just one of the useful functions of a small compressor. This particular inflator, which comes from a cheaper accessory kit, was prone to switching itself on when it was rested on the ground.

One of the most noticeable differences between spray guns is provided by the nozzle. On the left here is an external mix gun, whilst the one on the right is an internal mix example. Note also the difference in paint pot fixings, with the external mix gun having a plastic bayonet fit but the internal mix example requiring a more substantial screw thread fixing – to allow the pressurisation of the pot.

Spray guns like this one have just one control to alter the spray coverage from a narrow fan....

....to a wide one, simply by screwing it in or out. Such guns can cost anything between £15 and £30.

Compressors and their attachments

Basically, compressors come in three varieties – diaphragm, oil-less and wet piston. The diaphragm variety employ a neopropene or butal diaphragm and two reed valves worked by a connecting rod from the motor, which is electric. This type has few moving parts, making it virtually maintenance free which can be quite an advantage. The oil-less piston versions are similar in design and size to the diaphragm models, but they utilise a piston with a compression ring instead. These are also virtually maintenance free but have the added advantage of offering 50% more pressure and volume (cfm) – but of course they are more expensive. The third and final type, the wet piston compressor, is that found on tank compressors. In this type the piston has compression and oil control rings similar to those in a conventional petrol engine. The piston and its bearings are splash fed with oil from a sump, and this type of unit is usually fitted with an automatic pressure control system. This cuts off the motor once a pre-set maximum has been achieved, and re-starts it again when it falls to four-fifths of the original reading. This system, being more complex, does require a degree of maintenance, including changing the lubricating oil, cleaning the oil filter and draining the tank.

Draining a tank compressor means releasing the drain plug on the underside, to allow any collected water to escape (the tank should of course be emptied of compressed air before this is done). When air is compressed it loses its ability to hold water in suspension,

The Clarke Pioneer tank compressor represents a good example of a respectably powerful (3.75cfm, 115psi) unit for the home market. Its robust construction and upright stance make it ideal for a small garage or workshop. It features tank pressure and output pressure dials and an automatic cut-out system the same as the Kestrel C50/200D. This cut-out works at a pre-set maximum as a safety feature, and the motor is turned on again when the tank pressure falls to 4/5ths of the maximum.

This is an example of an oil-less compressor from Kestrel. They are much more powerful than the similarly sized diaphragm versions but are of course much more expensive. This one for example, comes as a kit with a hose and spray gun, and sells at a retail price of £301.12.

and therefore any water vapour present is compressed, the amount of water collected in the water trap increases, and it is this which must be relieved after use. It is important that the oil level is checked regularly and accurately, and that when the machine is switched on for the first time, that it is run for a few minutes with all valves open. This helps to ensure a good circulation of lubricant before any load is added.

Spray guns also come in a variety of differing types which include: constant bleed, non bleed, pressure feed, suction feed, gravity feed, internal mix and external mix. The constant bleed type of gun has no air control

This Jumbo compressor from Clarke has a variable output, but no gauge for accurate pressure readings. It too comes as part of a kit (with a hose and a suitable gun) and sells at a retail price of £123.00.

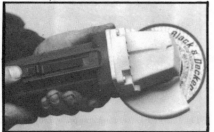

An electric angle grinder such as this (with a 5" wheel) is a most useful tool – it is both quick and effective. It runs at 10,000rpm and costs around £75+VAT. Always take great care to ensure that the guard is correctly positioned, and that the grinding wheel is not damaged in any way before you start grinding. Also, it is always best to wear gloves, and safety goggles are an absolute essential – with a grinding disc spinning at 10,000rpm it is wise not to take any chances. This tool can also be used for sanding and cutting.

valve, and is designed for use on constantly running compressors without a tank. These guns can be identified when connected up by the continuous hissing as the compressed air escapes. This effectively maintains a constant pressure in the gun and hose, and prevents the build of excessive pressure which would cause a surge when the gun was first operated. The constant flow of air also prevents the compressor from becoming over-loaded. The non-bleed type of gun does not allow a continuous flow of air through it, and is normally used with tank compressors. They feature a two-position trigger which when depressed slightly, opens the air valve prior to the paint being released, which helps to ensure that good atomisation of the paint occurs to produce a fine spray. The method by which the paint reaches the nozzle of the gun is known as the feed, and the three varieties differ in the following ways. Pressure feed occurs because the paint pot itself is pressurized, which forces the paint up the pick-up pipe and into the nozzle. This system relies on a tight seal being achieved between the pot and the gun body and so a screw thread is used on such guns rather than a bayonet fitting. Pressure feed guns are preferable for conditions where the air supply is limited, such as with small compressors, or when the material being sprayed is very thick.

Suction feed guns are more commonly used for high pressure spray work, and rely on a vortex drawing the paint up out of the pot and into the nozzle for their success. Such

guns do require a vented paint pot, and it is vital that this vent is kept clear. The final method of paint feed used is gravity feed, although this is more common on the Continent on full size guns. Its applications here extend only as far as customising or retouching guns, and as the name suggests, the paint is fed to the nozzle from a paint container above the gun, thanks to gravity. The final variation in spray gun specification concerns the paint mixing, and more precisely, where it occurs. To produce the fine spray required for specialist painting, the paint has to be subjected to a high speed stream of compressed air, and this either occurs inside the gun casing (internal mix), or just in front of the nozzle (external mix).

Constant bleed, pressure fed internal mix guns are usually coupled with diaphragm compressors, oil-less compressors are suited to suction fed, internal or external mix constant bleed guns and non bleed guns are compatible with tank compressors.

Safety and the law

Compressors, or more particularly their tanks, are potentially very dangerous pieces of apparatus. This fact is widely recognised amongst the legal profession concerned with industry, but unfortunately, in quite a number of cases the users are pitifully unaware of the legal requirements for the compressors, and for physical safety.

Black & Decker produce two ranges of tools, one designed for the DIY market, and the other for professional use and the prices between the two differ quite considerably. We sampled a professional two speed drill, and here it is shown in comparison to an elderly DIY version. The professional drill has a retail price of £87+VAT whereas its DIY counterpart can be bought for well under half that price. Extras that are included are a second handle, and a depth control bar.

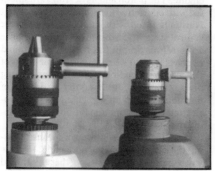

An interesting comparison between two specifications. The professional drill on the left is altogether more substantial.

Drills are always a bone of contention amongst metalworkers, but it appears to me that it is largely a case of how much you are prepared to spend. There are countless numbers of cheap sets on the market today, all of which could sell at about the same price. It is only the difference in packing and the number of drills per set that determine the price. The 29 piece Zak set shown here comes in a sturdy metal case and sells for a retail price of £33,35, whereas the 19 piece Hilka set sells for about £14 with only ten less drills. Your choice should really be influenced by what you intend to use the drills for. The cheap drills will blunt quickly and need replacing regularly, but on the other hand, an expensive drill can cost as much as a complete cheap set.

The Nibblex is a useful tool for cutting sheet metal and is easy to use. It sells for £15 plus VAT.

I took this opportunity to make some enquiries about this matter with a well known insurance company, and discovered the following. If you are a private owner and have a compressor in your garage for non-professional purposes, you appear to be exempt from both the Factory Act, and the Health and Safety at Work Act. However, as soon as you become a business and employ another person, you are governed by both Acts. This means that certificates will be required which can only be obtained after regular (every two years) inspection of the equipment. This appears to be true as far as the Factory Act is concerned, but the Health and Safety regulations are slightly different. I gather that they are presented as a series of recommendations which the person is

CONTINUED ON PAGE 74

Choosing and using a lathe

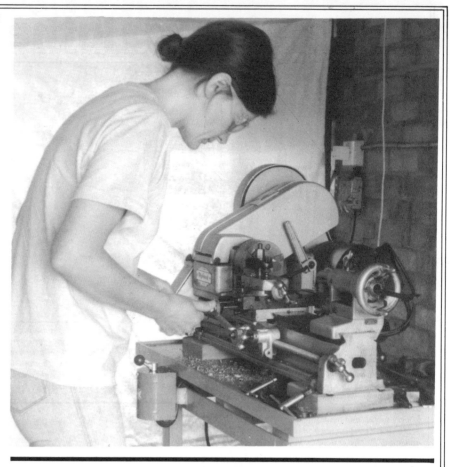

The centre lathe is a very versatile machine tool. Even simple ones are capable of producing cylindrical and flat surfaces, drilling holes and cutting internal and external screw threads. Most classic car restorers at some time have needed a shouldered bolt, small bush, or replacement shaft, and the lack of a lathe can result in an unrewarding search and a waste of time.

How the lathe works

The spindle (see the diagram of the parts of a lathe) is powered by an electric motor through a transmission system which may consist of belts and gears. The smaller the diameter of the workpiece the faster the spindle has to rotate. You will soon get a feel for the correct speed for the job. The spindle is connected to the leadscrew by a geartrain that can be changed to alter the ratio of spindle revolutions to leadscrew revolutions.

The saddle can be moved towards and away from the headstock either by hand or power. The tool can be moved shorter distances by using the top slide. Moving the tool in this way will produce external or internal

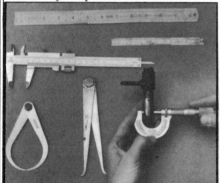

Accurate measurements being made on a Morris Minor brake pedal shaft prior to making a replacement. Take the measurements from an unworn component if possible – even experienced engineers have been known to measure, and then reproduce exactly, the worn components which they have been trying to replace. The measuring instruments which would be useful in conjunction with a lathe include calipers, steel rule, vernier calipers and micrometers.

John Vine offers advice which could help you to broaden the scope of your workshop.

cylindrical surfaces. A special tool called a boring bar will be needed for the internal surface. If the top slide is set over at an angle a conical surface will result.

If the saddle is kept stationary and the screw feed is operated either by hand, or, on more sophisticated machines, under power, a flat surface is produced, for example, when facing off the end of a bar. If a large component is being machined it can be fixed to the cross slide and machined with a tool mounted in the chuck called a fly cutter.

On some machines the saddle can be moved by rotating the leadscrew by means of a graduated handwheel fixed to its end. For this the leadscrew is not connected to the spindle.

The cross feed and top slide feed are graduated either in thousandths of an inch or hundredths of a millimetre. It is important to understand the implications of lost motion when operating the feeds. This backlash must be allowed for when turning. The feedhandle should move easily until the lost motion is taken up, and only then should the graduations be used.

Work can be mounted in many ways but must always be given as much support as possible to avoid 'chatter'. For short work the bar can be mounted directly in the chuck. Longer work will need tailstock support.

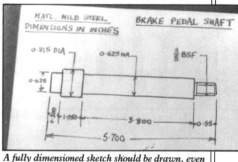

A fully dimensioned sketch should be drawn, even for simple components, before work commences.

This is achieved by mounting the bar in the chuck and drilling a small conical depression in its end using a special centre drill. It is best to face off the end of the bar beforehand. The tailstock is then adjusted to bring the dead (i.e. non-rotating) centre into the end of the bar. The centre should be oiled, and looked at periodically as work proceeds to check for overheating. Rotating centres are available.

If the bar is centre drilled at both ends it can be mounted between centres. The advantage of this method is that the workpiece can be removed from the lathe and replaced without loss of accuracy. The headstock centre is not hardened and can be machined to ensure

Choosing and using a lathe

Round, hexagonal and square bars of various sizes are available from steel stockholders and engineers merchants, but before buying metal have a look in your scrap box. Many old motor components such as half-shafts, kingpins and even larger bolts can be very useful (and free).

Hardened steel cannot be machined without first annealing it. This is done by heating it to red heat and then allowing it to cool very slowly. Do not make anything from mild steel that was originally made from a higher duty material.

Some lathe parts and accessories including (top left) three jaw chuck with spare jaws for internal gripping, (top right) four jaw chuck on which each jaw can be tightened individually, (bottom left) face with dividing pin and (bottom right) carriers in different sizes for different diameters.

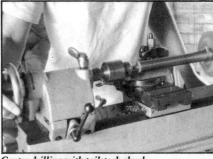

Centre drilling with tailstock chuck.

Work mounted between centres (soft in headstock, hard in tailstock). Don't forget to oil the tailstock centre and don't pinch it too tightly with the tailstock handwheel. Note that the driving pin in the faceplate is wired to the carrier with soft wire.

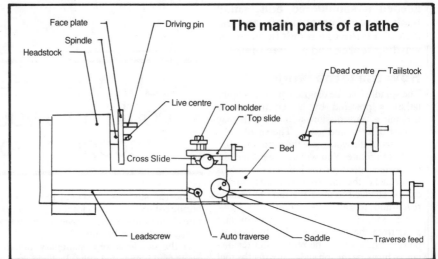

The main parts of a lathe

This is a selection of the cutting tools to be used in a lathe.

that its point coincides with the lathe's axis. Before fitting the carrier file a small flat on the bar to prevent slipping and wire the carrier to the driving pin with soft wire. Awkwardly shaped work can be bolted direct to the faceplate, or can be gripped in a four-jaw chuck where each jaw is reversible and independently tightened.

A word about lathe tools. These can be bought in sets, but it might be better to buy them as required. I have bought them from secondhand tool shops, autojumble stalls, etc. They may be solid tool steel, tungsten carbide tipped, or tungsten carbide tipped with replaceable tips. You will need a green grit sanding wheel to sharpen tungsten carbide. A tremendous amount of work has been done to ascertain the correct profile for a tool tip for each material and job, and trying to understand back rake, side rake, and top

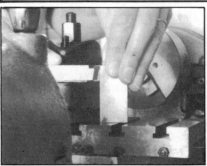

Having selected a suitable lathe tool it is mounted in the toolpost, and on this lathe it has to be shimmed to the correct height with metal packings. More sophisticated toolposts allow more rapid height adjustment.

rake can be difficult. For this reason regrind tools carefully in order to preserve their original profile. To minimise 'chatter', mount the tool firmly and with the minimum of overhang. Soluble cutting oils in an aerosol, or applied by brush, will improve the surface finish as will a very fine final cut. It the swarf

is coming off and turning blue you are taking too deep a cut or running at too high a speed, or both.

When using a parting tool for cutting off the finished job, lock the saddle to the bed.

It is essential to mount the tool so that its tip is exactly at centre height. Adjustment is normally provided by metal packing shims under the tool. A useful indication of whether the height is correct occurs when facing. If a pip is left in the middle, the height is wrong. A simple gauge, made to rest on the top slide, can also be used. The tool can also be lined up on the tailstock centre.

Drilling operations in the lathe are a little unusual in that the work rotates and the drill remains still. The drill is gripped in the tailstock chuck, or if taper shank drills are available, directly in the tailstock (and this is preferable). After facing and centre drilling the work a pilot hole is drilled, then the full size hole. The pilot hole can be omitted if the final hole is only ¼" or less in diameter. The depth of the hole is assessed by using the graduations on the tailstock barrel. Clear the

Choosing and using a lathe

A bar mounted in a 3-jaw chuck.

Checking diameter with vernier calipers. The bar should be turned until it is machined all over and to its full length. Measure the diameter with a micrometer or vernier calipers. Then subtract its intended diameter at its largest point and divide the result by 2. This is the amount that the tool must be advanced. It is useful to work the diameter down to within 2-3 thou of the desired measurement along about ¼" of the bar at the tailstock end first. In this way, if an error is made it will not ruin the whole bar. When this has been done satisfactorily machine along the whole bar using auto-traverse if available. The final cut should be very fine for the best surface finish.

Choosing a lathe

A number of factors will influence your choice of lathe, including the cost. If you can't afford a new machine perhaps you will find a secondhand lathe that will be suitable. The size of the lathe should be considered in relation to its intended use. Large lathes can be heavy and difficult to move, and most work on 3-phase electricity, so what might have seemed a secondhand bargain could

swarf frequently by withdrawing the drill.

Internal threads can be tapped by fitting the tap in the tailstock chuck and turning the lathe by hand. The tailstock will be advanced as thread cutting proceeds, so do not have it clamped to the bed.

External threads can be cut using a die mounted in a die holder that goes into the tailstock. Longer threads can be cut using the leadscrew and a tool ground to the profile of the thread being cut. This is 55° for Whitworth and BSF or 60° for the UNF and UNC gauges are available to aid tool grinding and setting the tool in the toolpost.

A rectangular block mounted in 4-jaw chuck and about to be drilled.

Specifications and prices of a selection of lathes

This table contains details of a representative selection of lathes, and it will give you a good idea of what can be obtained, new, for your money.

Maker of distributor	Country of origin	Model	Centre height	Distance between centres	Spindle hole	Spindle speeds	Weight	Power traverse	Power cross feed	Thread cutting	Price
Emco Maer Ltd 10 Woodshots Meadow Croxley Centre Watford Herts	Austria	Unimat 3	46mm	200mm	10.2mm	130/200 350/560 920/1500 2450/4000	7kg	No	No	As extra	£215 plus VAT including bed, headstock, tailstock, longitudinal and cross slides, tool holder, faceplate, lathe dog, 2 centres drive motor spanners instructions. Top slide is extra.
Emco Maer Ltd	Austria	Compact 5	65mm	350mm	16mm	200/330 550/950 1500/2400	20kg	As extra	No	As extra	£500 plus VAT including bed, headstock, tailstock, saddle and cross-slide with single tool holder, lathe dog, 2 centres drive motor, spanners. Top slide is extra.
Emco Maer Ltd	Austria	Compact 8	105mm	450mm	20mm	100/250 350/500 850/1700	58kg	Yes	No	As extra	£1205 plus VAT including bed, headstock, tailstock, saddle, cross and top slide, tailstock, driving pin, lathe dog, 2 centres toolholder, motor, tools and manual.
Myford Ltd Beeston Nottingham	Britain	ML 10	84mm	330mm	15.24mm	46/85 145/280 490/840	64kg	Yes	No	Yes	£750 plus VAT including bed, headstock, tailstock, saddle, cross and top slides, motor, reversing switch, 15 change wheels spanners, centres, 6" faceplate 4" 3-jaw chuck.
Myford Ltd	Britain	Super 7B 10/039	88.9mm	483mm	15mm	14 speed 27-2105 rpm	110kg approx.	Yes	Yes	Yes with quick change gearbox	£1737 plus VAT including motor, switch, countershaft clutch, leadscrew handwheel, faceplate, centres, 4" 3-jaw chuck spanners.
CZ Scientific Instruments 2 Elstree Way Borehamwood Herts		Robbymat MD 65	65mm	300mm	12mm	250/500 1000/2000	45kg	Yes	No	Yes	£365 plus VAT including top slide, motor, switch, tailstock, chuck, rotating centre, headstock centre, machine vice, angle plate, faceplate, spanners, changewheels, manual.
Peatol Machine Tools 19 Knightlow Rd Harbourne Birmingham	Britain	Peatol Micro lathe	2 1/4"	9 3/4"	0.343"	6 7000 rpm maximum	10kg approx	No	No	No	£181 including VAT 3 or 4-jaw chuck. tailstock motor drive. £6 less if self assemble. Top slide extra.
Wexler M/C Tools Wellspring Farmhouse Southrepps Norwich		Simat 101	50.5mm 66.5mm in gap	317mm bed	6.5mm	90 180 360 720 1440 rpm	9kg	Yes	No	No	£167.30 plus VAT including 4" faceplate centres, 4-way toolpost, top slide, tailstock, motor and drive. £18 less if self assemble.
Graham Engineering Ltd Roebuck Lane West Bromich Birmingham		Alpine 5MK	125mm	460mm	28mm	56-1800 rpm	190kg	Yes	Yes	Yes quick change gearbox	£1345 plus VAT including 3-jaw 5" chuck, centres, motor, drive, spanners, 4-way tool post, metric change gears.
Warren M/C Tools Middle Street, Shere, nr Guildford, Surrey	Taiwan	Warco 918	4 1/2"	18"				Yes	Yes	Yes quick change gearbox	£895 + VAT incl. 3 & 4-jaw chucks, fixed and travelling steadies 2 centres 4-way toolpost tools.

Choosing and using a **lathe**

To machine the end of a long bar it can be fed right through the spindle on some lathes.

The Peatol micro lathe.

Emco Compact 5.

prove to be expensive by the time that it is installed and working. On the other hand, there is little point in going to the trouble and expense of obtaining a lathe which could be used to skim a 13″ diamater flywheel if most of the work which you anticipate will be only 1-2″ in diameter.

It is particularly important when buying an old secondhand machine to find out what equipment comes with it, and to make enquiries about the availability of spares and accessories. Unless it is in running order and has full tooling it could be a bad buy.

Give some thought to the types of work which you hope to do with your lathe so that you will go shopping with a good idea of the minimum specification which will suit you. For example, some small lathes have no leadscrew, and screwcutting requires an additional accessory. On some lathes the top slide is an extra. Before you go shopping read all the literature you can get on current models.

Safety and a few practical hints

Lathes are expensive precision tools and yours should be treated with care and respect. Lubricate it correctly and grease any bare steel during damp conditions to prevent corrosion. Some lathes need oiling before every working sesson as well as regular greasing. Keep slides and feedscrew adjusted for minimum play. Keep the tools sharp and set to centre height.

Always wear safety glasses (swarf fragments can be both sharp and hot). Tie up long hair and secure all loose clothing. Use low voltage DC lighting. Fluorescent lights can produce a stroboscopic effect at certain spindle speeds which can be dangerous because it looks as if the spindle is stationary. Swarf can be razor sharp so don't handle it, but clear it up regularly and keep the lathe clean, espe-

The Warco 918 Model Engineers Lathe.

cially the bedways and leadscrew. A powerful vacuum cleaner is useful for this job.

Before switching on, rotate the spindle slowly by hand to ensure free movement. Don't leave the chuck key in the chuck. When working close to the headstock do not run the tool into the chuck.

Avoid using the lathe for grinding, as the grit particles are very abrasive.

If you are tempted to use a file when turning off sharp corners, make sure that it has a handle (you shouldn't be using a file without a handle in any case).

Be careful not to confuse radius and diameter. A micrometer will measure diameter but to work out how much further the tool needs to be moved the radius needs to be known.

Further reading

Introducing The Lathe by Stan Bray, published by Patrick Stephens Ltd.
Metal-Turning Lathes by E.T. Westbury, Model and Allied Publications Ltd.
Myford ML10 Lathe Manual by Ian Bradley, Model and Allied Publications Ltd.
The Action of Cutting Tools. The Machinery Publishing Co. Ltd.
Hardening And Tempering Engineers Tools. Model and Allied Publications Ltd.
Engineers And Machinists Reference Tables, Babani Press.

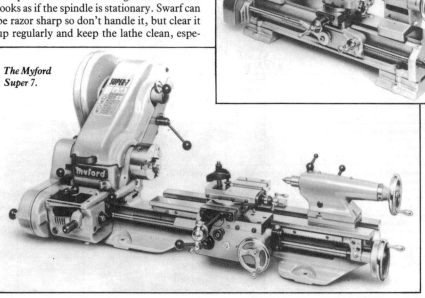

The Myford Super 7.

The Myford ML 10.

Reproduction Panels

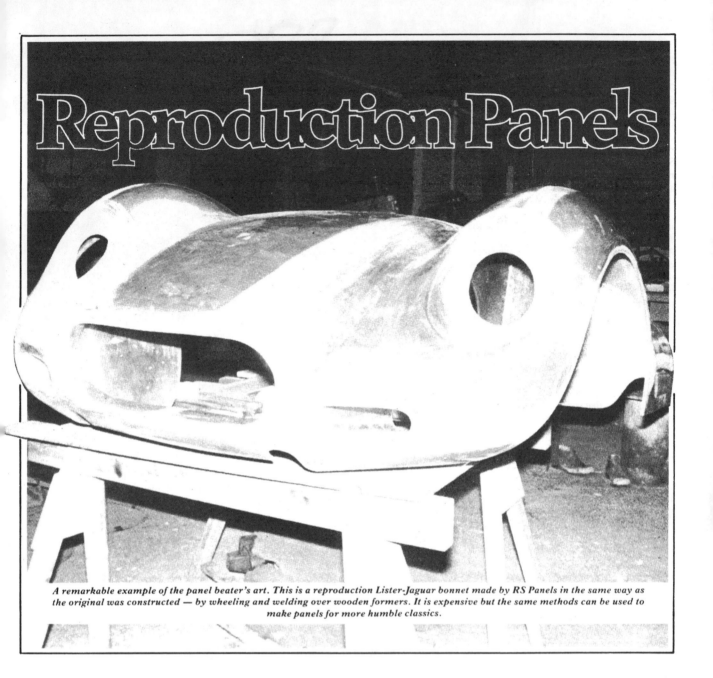

A remarkable example of the panel beater's art. This is a reproduction Lister-Jaguar bonnet made by RS Panels in the same way as the original was constructed — by wheeling and welding over wooden formers. It is expensive but the same methods can be used to make panels for more humble classics.

What goes into making them and why they have to cost so much. Michael Brisby reports.

At the end of the sixties I worked for Vauxhall Motors and the office I was kept in overlooked a sort of pound where huge lumps of metal, bigger than a man in every direction, were kept. From time to time groups of men would come over and use mobile cranes to re-arrange or remove a few rust streaked cubes. Being curious I asked what was going on and was told that those lumps of metal were the press tools used to make the panels for my out of date P.A. Cresta and that most of them had already been scrapped.

Last year I was shaken to hear that a man with two unused Cresta or Velox wings had been criticised for refusing to sell a pair for less than his £50 asking price. My mind went

back to those scrapped press tools — some of them weighing the best part of 14 tons — and I wondered whether some classic car owners realize just how precious unused factory body panels can be.

Most of the factory tooling which made the panels for our classic cars has been scrapped for many years, the only notable exception I

can think of being the tooling for the Jaguar E-type bonnets which the factory has retained so that they can meet a small but steady demand from grateful owners.

Creating tooling to press out body panels is an exacting and extremely costly process and it makes economic sense to accurately predict the required tool life with the aim that when the panel goes out of production the tooling is worn out and only fit for the limited runs of spare parts over a short term — perhaps four years.

Once a model goes out of production (always provided that the manufacturer is still in business) the manufacturer is not likely to sell the press tools until the spares requirement has been met. Here I must point out that a few hundred enthusiastic owners wishing to obtain new panels for restoration or repair purposes does not add up to a detectable demand in the eyes of the manufacturers.

While tooling is being used to produce spares requirement it is, or should be, at its most profitable point in its lifespan. By production standards it may be worn out — quality control of replacement body parts is generally much more lax than for the production line even when the model is current — but by this stage it will have been paid for as part of the cost of new cars sold. Spares production — free of tooling costs — means that once the tooling is set up, material and labour charges met and the parts made distributed the rest is profit. Making a guess I would suggest that most panels cost the manufacturer a quarter of what you pay at the spares counter.

If a manufacturer over-estimates the spares call and is left with stocks of any panels they will then have to consider the very high costs of warehousing bulky parts over an extended period and that is when the accountants call in the scrap metal merchants and we enthusiasts start protesting.

Once the manufacturer has no reason to retain the tooling which made our precious panels it might seem a good idea to make it available to the one-make car clubs, but very few firms outside the motor industry have suitable presses that can be made available and if a press with spare capacity *is* found there is still the problem of moving the tooling when it weighs several tons.

By the time most enthusiasts contemplate restoring a car, scenes like this line up of complete Spitfire bodyshells at the Triumph Warehouse are usually only dreams and once the supply of body panels dries up the manufacturer's tooling, if it is available, is generally of little practical value.

WHEN THERE IS NO TOOLING

Having, I hope, made the point that the manufacturer's tooling, if it was available, would probably not be of much use to enthusiasts or to the specialist concerns that cater for their old car needs, the obvious question is what do we do when supplies of body panels dry up? Fortunately there are some answers but the problem is that all but one of the solutions are expensive and call for special skills.

GLASS FIBRE

Glass fibre replacement panels are generally made from moulds obtained from an original panel and a good quality moulding is generally fairly accurate, free of ripples and reasonably durable. The advantages of Fibreglass panels include low cost (often lower than original panels), availability (particularly for non-exotic cars but largely restricted to front wings) and long life barring mishaps. The disadvantages of glass fibre panels are that even bolted on steel external panels offer better resistance to impact damage than most g.r.p. panels and lopping even rusty panels off to make way for glass-fibre ones could rob a car of vital strength.

CHEAP, SHORT TERM TOOLING

It is possible to create short-run press-tooling in hard rubber. There are probably limitations on what panels can be made on such tooling and it is not a cheap method. I have seen extremely authentic looking pressings made by this system but it is not widely used and

information about it is hard to come by. Even if rubber tooling is viable it still requires very substantial industrial presses.

OTHER METHODS

For many years people have admired the beautiful shapes Italian designers and craftsmen created for the bodies of all sorts of exotic cars — yes, for Ferraris in particular! What many people do not realize is that if they saw the beautiful bodies in bare metal they would often see that all the panels with a lot of form whether it be in compound curves or angles are made up from a patchwork quilt of small sections beaten to shape by hand, using wooden mallets and sand-bags or suitably

The impressive array of hand tools a skilled man uses to make panels by hand — (l-r) body file, slappers, hammers, universal, left and right cut tin snips, dollies and more hammers including a wooden mallet.

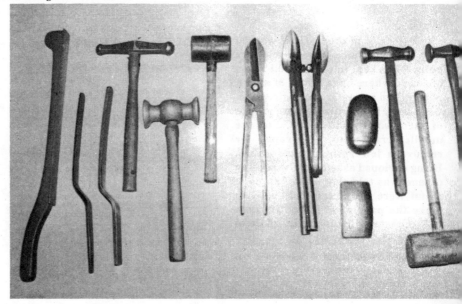

shaped blocks of wood and then welded together to form a whole.

Metal is like pastry in that its shape can be altered by compressing or expanding its thickness and this can be demonstrated by taking a flat sheet of steel or aluminium and placing it on a firm surface. If you hit the metal with the ball pein of an engineer's hammer it will distort locally and if you go on to form a circle of impacts on that same sheet you will see it begin to form a bowl — that is the basic principal behind making a panel or a small section of a panel without using press tools.

Getting the distortion to work *for* you, so that the metal goes where you want, is an art but provided the determined home enthusiast has enough evidence in the shape of an original wing mounted on the car and only tackles small areas at a time, even a very rotten wing can be repaired with serviceable results

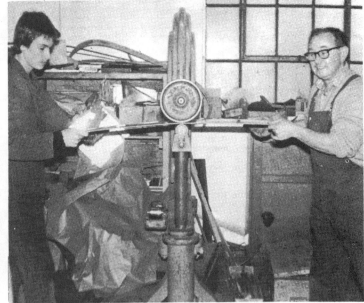

The wheeling machine is deceptively simple. To master it requires natural ability and considerable experience. The wheels or rollers the metal sheet is passed between can be changed as required but the pressure between them and the number and direction of passes between them affect the development of the sections being made. The wheels must be very accurately machined to maintain a constant gap between them.

— you will not need a lot of equipment (gas welding gear is essential) but you must have a good eye and a great deal of patience!

WHEELING

I have already stated that if you squeeze areas of sheet metal that metal will distort. This squeezing effect can be achieved by using a mallet to hit the metal while it is rested on a sand bag or block of wood — but a refinement of this method is to pass the metal between two rollers. Such an arrangement is known as a wheeling machine.

For such a very simple looking device the wheeling machine is extraordinarily difficult to use. We spoke to Bob Smith of R.S. Panels (well-known for their expertise in making both panels and complete bodies) but he quickly dismissed any suggestion that it takes years to learn to wheel. "The better wheelers are lads that have a natural ability for that sort of thing, a flair for being artistic if you like. You can't teach it, the only way people are going to learn wheeling is by doing it, it is only experience that will teach you. You can stand and watch somebody all day if you like but it won't mean a thing to you — it's only when you do it yourself and begin to understand what is happening to the metal that you will get anywhere, *if* you have the ability."

The chances of any amateur restorers discovering whether they have the ability to wheel metal are few and far between because what wheeling machines there are, are generally snapped up by those with a commercial interest, and usually cost several hundred pounds secondhand.

The shape produced by passing sheet metal through a wheeling machine depends upon several factors including the rollers fitted (the operator has a selection to choose from) the tension between the rollers and the number of times and direction in which the metal is passed through the machine. Once you know

what result your actions with this deceptively simple looking machine are going to produce, you can start making panels.

A PATTERN

The obvious pattern for a reproduction panel is a factory original panel, whether it is one that has survived unused, or a rusty (but straight) one firmly attached to a car. If the specialist intends to produce a series of high quality copies he will use that original panel to make a jig or buck (often using wood); if, however, the intention is to make a very small number or quality is less important, the original will be used as a direct pattern.

A "direct pattern" is my own term , and by it I mean that the panel maker will make his reproduction copy over the top of the original panel. I have seen original wings that have been in use as patterns for years — they flop about as another "new" wing is created over

the top of them and bear the scars of having countless other copies hammered to fit closely over the top of them. Whether or not the original wing is now the correct shape and whether the panel maker makes adjustments to reduce the reproduction panels to the correct dimensions is somewhat debatable and explains why some reproduction panels are so difficult to fit. A panel specialist anxious to produce a good product will construct a jig or buck if he intends making more than a handful of copies.

R.S. Panels have found it worthwhile to construct jigs for the complete bodies for both the Lister-Jaguar "knobbly" body and the C-type Jaguar because the demand (although strictly limited) and the overall cost of constructing new bodies for these valuable cars makes such an exercise viable. It should be added that the complexity of the shapes and the fact that nobody in his right mind would allow reproduction panels to be beaten over

A wooden C-type Jaguar body! This is the jig or buck on which R.S. Panels make reproduction C-type bodywork. The panel sections are tied on like clothing on a tailor's dummy and are not beaten to shape on the jig although the solid timber construction on some critical points allows fine adjustments to be made with the panels mounted. Construction of such jigs is understandably expensive.

This is R.S. Panels' jig or buck for a Jaguar XK150 rear wing. For the production of small numbers of panels a skilled man can work from an original panel, however.

such valuable originals contributed to these decisions!

As can be seen from the photographs the jigs or bucks provide three dimensional templates of the panel cross-sections and some of the areas where there are sharp radius curves are made of solid wood.

THE JIG-SAW

Close examination of many factory panels, particularly those with a lot of curvatuous form will reveal that even panels that are pressed out are often made up in separate sections and then welded together to form what at first glance appears to be a continuous sheet of metal. Dependent upon the nature of the sheet metal used, the form required, the area of metal to be worked and the time available to work it, there are limitations to what even a very complex sequence of pressing processes or wheeling operations can do to one sheet of metal. It therefore follows that press tool designers or the reproduction panel maker has to look at the required panel and mentally cut it up into what is practical to achieve.

In general where the metal changes direction in gentle curves the panel can be

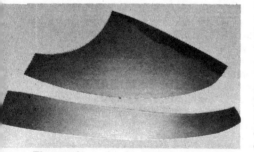

The starting point for the rear part of the Jaguar rear wing — two shapes cut from flat steel sheet.

The same two pieces carefully welded together have already begun to assume the desired shape before any beating or wheeling has been carried out because the two sections were cut out of the sheet correctly. In this case the same shape could have been achieved by wheeling but it would have taken longer and cost the customer more.

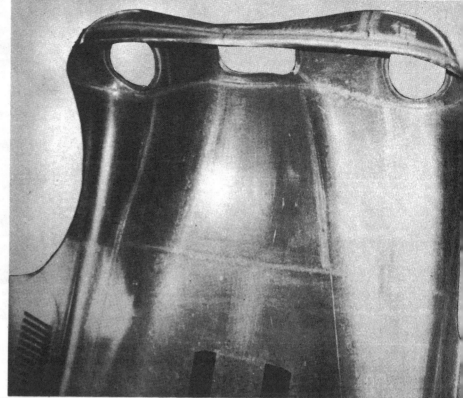

It is quite impossible to make a complex item like this Jaguar C-type bonnet in one piece — we have counted fourteen sections welded together in this view of the underbonnet.

made up in large sections — for reproduction purposes as large as one panel beater can handle on the wheeling machine. Where the metal is required to assume a number of directions within a small area a number of small sections will be made up and welded together.

Clearly it takes considerable skill to know how to plan the sections needed to create a panel so that the shapes required are feasable to make, and the welds occur in positions where they can be beaten smooth. Even cutting the flat sheet of metal so that once it has been distorted into a three dimensional shape its outer perimeter will be compatable with its neighbouring section is something that has to be taken into consideration.

MATERIALS

Given a sheet of steel and a sheet of aluminium of the same thickness and asked to make the same three dimensional shape out of it the panel beater will make the aluminium component quicker and therefore more cheaply because the aluminium is softer and more pliable. However, while aluminium is lighter and does not rust it is also not immune to corrosion (especially when exposed to salt or placed adjacent to steel) it cracks or rips more readily than steel and it dents easily particularly if not protected from stones thrown at it by the car's wheels.

Other considerations for those tempted by the possibility that reproduction panels in aluminium will be cheaper than those made in steel are strength and originality. Most mass-produced cars made since the Second World War have been bodied in steel and in many cases the outer panels have contributed to the structural strength of the car. Before seizing upon the chance to have cheaper panels that will not rust, some thought should be given to whether replacing steel with aluminium is acceptable structurally.

If you own an Austin Healey (non-Sprite) where the front and rear shrouds were made of aluminium or an MGA where the bonnet, boot-lid and doors were skinned in aluminium there may be a strong temptation — on the grounds of weight-saving, resistance to rust and cost-saving — to complete your restoration project by clapping on a good set of faithful reproduction alloy wings at say, £425 a set as opposed to around £500 for steel items. The most immediate drawback is that unless you provide protection, flying stones will dimple the wings and later on, if you decide to sell the car you could find that originality conscious prospective buyers deduct £500 from their offers as a contribution towards buying, fitting and painting a set of correct steel wings!

SPOT THE JOIN!

Whether the reproduction panel is to be made in steel or alloy the methods employed by the panel beater are the same. Each section of the whole panel is folded, rolled or wheeled to achieve the correct contour by matching it to the panel serving as a pattern or the jig — the process could be likened to re-fitting the shell to a hard boiled egg except that the panel beater is making the shell from flat sheets of metal!

You have not seen welding until you have seen a skilled panel maker linking the component sections of a panel — the best men

The weld between the two sections was crushed before using the wheel to introduce more curvature to the top edge.

A crimping tool being used to contract the outer edge and introduce still more curve to the wing's cross-section.

The forward section of the same wing is made up from one piece of metal with a "dart" cut out to assist in achieving the desired shape although most of the work is done by wheeling, and with frequent reference to the jig.

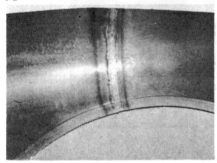

The front and rear sections of the Jaguar wing welded together.

create remarkably long continuous welds with a small weld bead and not a trace of undercutting. The weld bead and any unavoidable distortion along the joint is then removed by crushing the weld through the wheeling machine, hammering, filing and sanding until you have to have a very good eye to see where the joints are. I have seen one unpainted body made by a craftsman where I had to look inside the body very closely to see where the traces of the joints in the panels were — you could not tell from the outside! The reverse of that story occured when I tackled the repair of a one-off bonnet from an Italian coachbuilder (Frua). When we stripped the paint off the bonnet we had to remove a thick layer of primer-filler and once we got it off you could see both the gas welds and the depressions left by spot welding. In that case the only way to disguise the imperfections on the repaired bonnet was to adopt the Italian's short-cut and put on a thick coat of primer-filler!

The swage line that created a rebate into which the wheel spat on disc wheel XK Jaguars fitted was common to all XK wings (including those on cars that did not have spats) and is being introduced to the wheel arch edge here. The machine has two suitably shaped rollers (the inner one is hidden by the wing).

Details like these cooling louvres are generally made on a fly press from a flat sheet of metal which is then welded into the body section.

A partially recessed light housing like this may look relatively simple but getting such details correct is a skilled operation and adds to the cost of making a panel.

FITTING

One of the things that you learn the hard way when restoring even mass-produced cars is that in most cases there is no such thing as a "correct" body dimension. In many cases there are such unexpected surprises as long and short wings, and doors and bonnets which have been tailored for a particular car and are not interchangeable. On one occasion in the workshop I worked in we set out to make a template to enable us to consistently obtain the correct alignment of panels at the rear of E-type Jaguars. With five apparently undamaged and un-restored cars in front of us, we found that no two were the same — so we promptly abandoned thoughts of finding identical E-types and went back to doing it "by eye". On hand-made cars the chances of finding identical examples are non-existent so it follows that a hand-made reproduction panel is unlikely to fit straight on unless the man making the panel had the car in front of him — it is the difference between a tailor made and an "off-the-peg" suit.

Most of the so-called "panel-beaters" in the garage trade are unable or unwilling to expend the time, patience and skill needed to fit a reproduction panel to an old car. Anyone restoring a car should seek advice firstly amongst fellow owners who can suggest which specialist makes panels which are accurate, and secondly, about how to fit them. Whatever you do, do not attempt to make drastic alterations without first consulting the people who made the panels. Almost without exception they take enormous pride in the skills they exercise to create panels from the flat sheet and their pride usually extends to being only too willing to suggest how you should go about overcoming fitting problems. □

Metalworking Part 16 _____ Continued

advised to adhere to, but they can be ignored. If this is the case and something goes wrong though, you are in deep trouble, so the motto is play it by the book.

Another interesting point to come out of our discussion concerned the stamping of units with the BS 5169 mark. This is a British Standard stamp and can usually be considered a fairly safe guarantee of the equipment's quality. However, there are exceptions; in March 1981 an amendment was made to the Standard which stated that the legs and motor could no longer be welded directly to the shell of the air tank, as this created a risk of stress fracturing. The new ruling stated that metal discs had first to be welded to the tank, and then the legs and motor welded on to these so that a form of insulation was created – thus the discs would crack rather than the tank casing. This is all well and good for those manufacturers who have met the improved standards, and stamped their units accordingly, but there are units being made without these protective insulator discs which are still being stamped BS 5169, and this is naughty. However, it is easy to check for this visually, so there should be few problems here. For the precise rulings concerning this type of stamping, and the legal liability to the two Acts mentioned, it is best to consult your insurance broker, who, once he knows what your position is, will advise on the correct course of action.

We were most impressed with this Bosch Cordless Drill/Screwdriver in all respects. It was an immediaely likeable tool with a surprising amount of power. The motor can be run forwards or in reverse, and there are two speeds for both gears. Bosch recommend that the largest diameters that can be successfully drilled are 10mm in steel, and 15mm in wood.

It comes complete with a screwdriver bit which although looking a little weedy, proved quite adequate in the tests we performed, and a chuck key – both of which are mounted neatly in recesses in the casing. The battery pack was easily detachable and its charger was simple to use, although we did feel that it would have benefited from a 'charging' light. On this 'amateur' model the battery takes 12 hours to charge fully, but the Professional models boast a 1 hour charging time. This type of tool is expensive (£80 or so), but the sheer convenience of the cordless specification makes them very tempting, especially once you have tried one out.

Electric tools

As I said earlier, the high level of expense involved in the purchase of specialist air tools has allowed the electrical manufacturers to flourish. People have no real alternative at present, apart of course, from the cordless tools, which provide a very interesting option but at a price. With the conventional electric tools one is always up against the inconvenience created by the need for long extension cables which as well as being a nuisance, can be dangerous. However, this is compensated for by the ease with which they can be bought and used.

It should be noted that all the prices quoted here are the retail prices, and that considerable reductions on most of them will be found if you shop around.

Special thanks to: Robert Bosch Limited, Power Tools Division, PO Box 98, Broadwater Park, North Orbital Road, Denham, Uxbridge, Middx, UB9 5HJ; Clarke Group, Lower Clapton Road, Hackney, London, E5 0RN, telephone 01-986 8231; Kestrel Equipment Ltd, Unit C, 72/78 Station Road, Shalford, nr Guildford, Surrey, GU4 8HD; and to Transpeed (Mail Order) Limited, 213 Portland Road, Hove, East Sussex, BN3 5LA, telephone 0273 774578, for the loan of equipment and the technical information which made this feature possible. □

TITLES IN THIS SERIES

Available From:

'Practical Classics', Kelsey House, 77 High Street, Beckenham Kent BR3 1AN   Brooklands Book Distribution Ltd, holmerise, Seven Hills Road, Cobham, Surrey, KT11 1ES UK. Tel: Cobham (0932) 65051

Take Our Advice And Do It Yourself.

practical CLASSICS Only 'Practical Classics' gives you really detailed, down-to-earth guidance on the maintenance, repair and restoration of your classic or older (pre-1972) car.

practical CLASSICS No other publication covers the subject so comprehensively, gives you so much helpful advice.

practical CLASSICS Regular monthly articles include:

TOTAL RESTORATIONS • TECHNIQUES • SPARES AVAILABILITY • GUIDE TO CAR VALUES • MONEY-SAVING SPECIAL OFFERS • BUYING SECONDHAND • COMPETITIONS

practical CLASSICS

THE ONLY DO-IT-YOURSELF MAGAZINE FOR THE CLASSIC AND OLDER-CAR ENTHUSIAST

From your newsagent on the second Thursday of the month.

practical CLASSICS & Car Restorer

SPECIAL OFFER! Famous Vices

RILEY RMF DIY REBUILD
MACHINE SHOP INSIDE VIEW
FAST Mk I ESCORTS: A BUYERS GUIDE
OUR SPITFIRE ON THE ROAD

BROOKLANDS ROAD TEST SERIES

AC Ace & Aceca 1953-1983
Alfa Romeo Alfasud 1972-1984
Alfa Romeo Alfetta Coupes GT, GTV, GTV6 1974-1987
Alfa Romeo Giulia Berlinas 1962-1976
Alfa Romeo Giulia Coupes 1963-1976
Alfa Romeo Giulietta Gold Portfolio 1954-1965
Alfa Romeo Spider 1966-1990
Allard Gold Portfolio 1937-1958
Alvis Gold Portfolio 1919-1958
American Motors Muscle Cars 1966-1970
Armstrong Siddeley Gold Portfolio 1945-1960
Aston Martin Gold Portfolio 1972-1985
Austin Seven 1922-1982
Austin A30 & A35 1951-1962
Austin Healey 100 & 100/6 Gold Portfolio 1952-1959
Austin Healey 3000 Gold Portfolio 1959-1967
Austin Healey 'Frogeye' Sprite Col No.1 1958-1961
Austin Healey Sprite 1958-1971
Avanti 1962-1983
BMW Six Cylinder Coupes 1969-1975
BMW 1600 Col. 1 1966-1981
BMW 2002 1968-1976
Bristol Cars Gold Portfolio 1946-1985
Buick Automobiles 1947-1960
Buick Muscle Cars 1965-1970
Buick Riviera 1963-1978
Cadillac Automobiles 1949-1959
Cadillac Automobiles 1960-1969
Cadillac Eldorado 1967-1978
High Performance Capris Gold Portfolio 1969-1987
Chevrolet Camaro SS & Z28 1966-1973
Chevrolet Camaro & Z-28 1973-1981
High Performance Camaros 1982-1988
Camaro Muscle Cars 1966-1972
Chevrolet 1955-1957
Chevrolet Corvair 1959-1969
Chevrolet Impala & SS 1958-1971
Chevrolet Muscle Cars 1966-1971
Chevelle and SS 1964-1972
Chevy Blazer 1969-1981
Chevy EL Camino & SS 1959-1987
Chevy II Nova & SS 1962-1973
Chrysler 300 1955-1970
Citroen Traction Avant Gold Portfolio 1934-1957
Citroen DS & ID 1955-1975
Citroen SM 1970-1975
Citroen 2CV 1949-1982
Shelby Cobra Gold Portfolio 1962-1969
Cobras & Replicas 1962-1983
Chevrolet Corvette Gold Portfolio 1953 1962
Corvette Stingray Gold Portfolio 1963-1967
High Performance Corvettes 1983-1989
Daimler SP250 Sport & V-8250 Saloon Gold Portfolio 1959-1969
Datsun 240Z 1970-1973
Datsun 280Z & ZX 1975-1983
De Tomaso Collection No.1 1962-1981
Dodge Charger 1966-1974
Dodge Muscle Cars 1967-1970
Excalibur Collection No.1 1952-1981
Facel Vega 1954-1964
Ferrari Cars 1946-1956
Ferrari Cars 1973-1977
Ferrari Dino 1965-1974
Ferrari Dino 308 1974-1979
Ferrari 308 & Mondial 1980-1984
Ferrari Collection No.1 1960-1970
Fiat-Bertone X1/9 1973-1988
Fiat Pininfarina 124 + 2000 Spider 1968-1985
Ford Automobiles 1949-1959
Ford Bronco 1966-1977
Ford Bronco 1978-1988
Ford Consul, Zephyr Zodiac Mk1 & II 1950-1962
Ford Cortina 1600E & GT 1967-1970
Ford Fairlane 1955-1970
Ford Falcon 1960-1970
Ford GT40 Gold Portfolio 1964-1987
Ford RS Escorts 1968-1980
Ford Zephyr Zodiac Executive MkIII & MkIV 1962-1971
High Performance Escorts Mk1 1968-1974
High Performance Escorts Mk II 1975-1980
High Performance Mustangs 1982-1988
Holden 1948-1962
Honda CRX 1983-1987
Hudson & Railton 1936-1940
Jaguar and SS Gold Portfolio 1931-1951
Jaguar Cars 1957-1961
Jaguar Cars 1961-1964
Jaguar Mk2 1959-1969
Jaguar E-Type Gold Portfolio 1961-1971
Jaguar E-Type 1966-1971
Jaguar E-Type V-12 1971-1975
Jaguar XKE Collection No.1 1961-1974
Jaguar XJ6 1968-1972
Jaguar XJ6 Series II 1973-1979
Jaguar XJ6 & XJ12 Series III 1979-1985
Jaguar XJ12 1972-1980
Jaguar XJS Gold Portfolio 1975-1988
Jaguar XK120,XK140,XK150 Gold Portfolio 1948-1960
Jeep CJ5 & CJ6 1960-1976
Jeep CJ5 & CJ7 1976-1986
Jensen Cars 1946-1967
Jensen Cars 1967-1979
Jensen Interceptor Gold Portfolio 1966-1986
Jensen Healey 1972-1976
Lamborghini Cars 1964-1970
Lamborghini Cars 1970-1975
Lamborghini Countach Col No.1 1971-1982
Lamborghini Countach & Urraco 1974-1980
Lamborghini Countach & Jalpa 1980-1985
Lancia Stratos 1972-1985
Land Rover 1948-1973 - A Collection
Land Rover Series II & IIa 1958-1971
Land Rover Series III 1971-1985
Land Rover 90 & 110 1983-1989
Lincoln Gold Portfolio 1949-1960
Lincoln Continental 1961-1969
Lotus and Caterham Seven Gold Portfolio 1957-1989
Lotus Cortina Gold Portfolio 1963-1970
Lotus Elan Gold Portfolio 1962-1974
Lotus Elan Collection No.2 1963-1972
Lotus Elite 1957-1964
Lotus Elite & Eclat 1974-1982
Lotus Turbo Esprit 1980-1986
Lotus Europa 1966-1975
Lotus Europa Collection No.1 1966-1974

Lotus Seven Collection No.1 1957-1982
Marcos Cars 1960-1988
Maserati 1965-1970
Maserati 1970-1975
Mazda RX-7 Collection No.1 1978-1981
Mercedes 190 & 300SL 1954-1963
Mercedes 230/250/280SL 1963-1971
Mercedes Benz SLs & SLCs Gold Portfolio 1971-1989
Mercedes Bens Cars 1949-1954
Mercedes Bens Cars 1954-1957
Mercedes Bens Cars 1957-1961
Mercedes Bens Cars 1966-1971
Mercedes Bens Competition Cars 1950-1957
Mercury Muscle Cars 1966-1971
Metropolitan 1954-1962
MG TC 1945-1949
MG TD 1949-1953
MG TF 1953-1955
MG Cars 1959-1962
MGA Roadsters 1955-1962
MGA Collection No.1 1955-1982
MGB Roadsters 1962-1980
MGB GT 1965-1980
MG Midget 1961-1980
Mini Cooper Gold Portfolio 1961-1971
Mini Moke 1964-1989
Mini Muscle Cars 1965-1979
Mopar Muscle Cars 1964-1967
Mopar Muscle Cars 1968-1971
Morgan Three-Wheeler Gold Portfolio 1910-1952
Morgan Cars 1960-1970
Morgan Cars Gold Portfolio 1968-1989
Morris Minor Collection No.1
Mustang Muscle Cars 1967-1971
Oldsmobile Automobiles 1955-1963
Old's Cutlass & 4-4-2 1964-1972
Oldsmobile Muscle Cars 1964-1971
Oldsmobile Toronado 1966-1978
Opel GT 1968-1973
Packard Gold Portfolio 1946-1958
Pantera Gold Portfolio 1970-1989
Plymouth Barracuda 1964-1974
Plymouth Muscle Cars 1966-1971
Pontiac Tempest & GTO 1961-1965
Pontiac GTO 1964-1970
Pontiac Firebird 1967-1973
Pontiac Firebird and Trans-Am 1973-1981
High Performance Firebirds 1982-1988
Pontiac Fiero 1984-1988
Pontiac Muscle Cars 1966-1972
Porsche 356 1952-1965
Porsche Cars in the 60's
Porsche Cars 1960-1964
Porsche Cars 1964-1968
Porsche Cars 1968-1972
Porsche Cars 1972-1975
Porsche Turbo Collection No.1 1975-1980
Porsche 911 1965-1969
Porsche 911 1970-1972
Porsche 911 1973-1977
Porsche 911 Carrera 1973-1977
Porsche 911 Turbo 1975-1984
Porsche 911 SC 1977-1983
Porsche 914 Gold Portfolio 1969-1976
Porsche 914 Collection No.1 1969-1983
Porsche 924 Gold Portfolio 1975-1988
Porsche 928 1977-1989
Porsche 944 1981-1985
Range Rover Gold Portfolio 1970-1988
Reliant Scimitar 1964-1986
Riley 11/2 & 21/2 Litre Gold Portfolio 1945-1955
Rolls Royce Silver Cloud 1955-1965
Rolls Royce Silver Shadow 1965-1981
Rover P4 1949-1959
Rover P4 1955-1964
Rover 3 & 3.5 Litre 1958-1973
Rover 2000 + 2200 1963-1977
Rover 3500 1968-1977
Rover 3500 & Vitesse 1976-1986
Saab Sonett Collection No.1 1966-1974
Saab Turbo 1976-1983
Shelby Mustang Muscle Cars 1965-1970
Stubebaker Gold Portfolio 1947-1966
Stubebaker Hawks & Larks 1956-1963
Sunbeam Tiger & Alpine Gold Portfolio 1959-1967
Thunderbird 1955-1957
Thunderbird 1958-1963
Thunderbird 1964-1976
Toyota Land Cruiser 1956-1984
Toyota MR2 1984-1988
Triumph 2000, 2.5, 2500 1963-1977
Triumph GT6 1966-1974
Triumph Spitfire 1962-1980
Triumph Spitfire Col No.1 1962-1982
Triumph Stag 1970-1980
Triumph Stag Collection No.1 1970-1984
Triumph TR2 & TR3 1952-60
Triumph TR4-TR5-TR250 1961-1968
Triumph TR6 1969-1976
Triumph TR6 Collection No.1 1969-1983
Triumph TR7 & TR8 1975-1982
Triumph Herald 1959-1971
Triumph Vitesse 1962-1971
TVR Gold Portfolio 1959-1988
Volkswagen Cars 1936-1956
VW Beetle Collection No.1 1970-1982
VW Golf GTI 1976-1986
VW Karmann Ghia 1955-1982
VW Scirocco 1974-1981
VW Bus, Camper, Van 1954-1967
VW Bus, Camper, Van 1968-1979
VW Bus, Camper, Van 1979-1989
Volvo 120 1956-1970
Volvo 1800 1960-1973

BROOKLANDS ROAD & TRACK SERIES

Road & Track on Alfa Romeo 1949-1963
Road & Track on Alfa Romeo 1964-1970
Road & Track on Alfa Romeo 1971-1976
Road & Track on Alfa Romeo 1977-1989
Road & Track on Aston Martin 1962-1984
Road & Track on Auburn Cord and Duesenburg 1952-1984
Road & Track on Audi & Auto Union 1952-1980
Road & Track on Audi 1980-1986
Road & Track on Austin Healey 1953-1970

Road & Track on BMW Cars 1966-1974
Road & Track on BMW Cars 1975-1978
Road & Track on BMW Cars 1979-1983
Road & Track on Cobra, Shelby & GT40 1962-1983
Road & Track on Corvette 1953-1967
Road & Track on Corvette 1968-1982
Road & Track on Corvette 1982-1986
Road & Track on Datsun Z 1970-1983
Road & Track on Ferrari 1950-1968
Road & Track on Ferrari 1968-1974
Road & Track on Ferrari 1975-1981
Road & Track on Ferrari 1981-1984
Road & Track on Fiat Sports Cars 1968-1987
Road & Track on Jaguar 1950-1960
Road & Track on Jaguar 1961-1968
Road & Track on Jaguar 1968-1974
Road & Track on Jaguar 1974-1982
Road & Track on Jaguar 1983-1989
Road & Track on Lamborghini 1964-1985
Road & Track on Lotus 1972-1981
Road & Track on Maserati 1952-1974
Road & Track on Maserati 1975-1983
Road & Track on Mazda RX7 1978-1986
Road & Track on Mercedes 1952-1962
Road & Track on Mercedes 1963-1970
Road & Track on Mercedes 1971-1979
Road & Track on Mercedes 1980-1987
Road & Track on MG Sports Cars 1949-1961
Road & Track on MG Sprots Cars 1962-1980
Road & Track on Mustang 1964-1977
Road & Track on Nissan 300-ZX & Turbo 1984-1989
Road & Track on Peugeot 1955-1986
Road & Track on Pontiac 1960-1983
Road & Track on Porsche 1951-1967
Road & Track on Porsche 1968-1971
Road & Track on Porsche 1972-1975
Road & Track on Porsche 1975-1978
Road & Track on Porsche 1979-1982
Road & Track on Porsche 1982-1985
Road & Track on Porsche 1985-1988
Road & Track on Rolls Royce & B'ley 1950-1965
Road & Track on Rolls Royce & B'ley 1966-1984
Road & Track on Saab 1955-1985
Road & Track on Toyota Sports & GT Cars 1966-1984
Road & Track on Triumph Sports Cars 1953-1967
Road & Track on Triumph Sports Cars 1967-1974
Road & Track on Triumph Sports Cars 1974-1982
Road & Track on Volkswagen 1951-1968
Road & Track on Volkswagen 1968-1978
Road & Track on Volkswagen 1978-1985
Road & Track on Volvo 1957-1974
Road & Track on Volvo 1975-1985
Road & Track - Henry Manney at Large and Abroad

BROOKLANDS CAR AND DRIVER SERIES

Car and Driver on BMW 1955-1977
Car and Driver on BMW 1977-1985
Car and Driver on Cobra, Shelby & Ford GT 40 1963-1984
Car and Driver on Corvette 1956-1967
Car and Driver on Corvette 1968-1977
Car and Driver on Corvette 1978-1982
Car and Driver on Corvette 1983-1988
Car and Driver on Datsun Z 1600 & 2000 1966-1984
Car and Driver on Ferrari 1955-1962
Car and Driver on Ferrari 1963-1975
Car and Driver on Ferrari 1976-1983
Car and Driver on Mopar 1956-1967
Car and Driver on Mopar 1968-1975
Car and Driver on Mustang 1964-1972
Car and Driver on Pontiac 1961-1975
Car and Driver on Porsche 1955-1962
Car and Driver on Porsche 1963-1970
Car and Driver on Porsche 1970-1976
Car and Driver on Porsche 1977-1981
Car and Driver on Porsche 1982-1986
Car and Driver on Saab 1956-1985
Car and Driver on Volvo 1955-1986

BROOKLANDS PRACTICAL CLASSICS SERIES

PC on Austin A40 Restoration
PC on Land Rover Restoration
PC on Metalworking in Restoration
PC on Midget/Sprite Restoration
PC on Mini Cooper Restoration
PC on MGB Restoration
PC on Morris Minor Restoration
PC on Sunbeam Rapier Restoration
PC on Triumph Herald/Vitesse
PC on Triumph Spitfire Restoration
PC on VW Beetle Restoration
PC on 1930s Car Restoration

BROOKLANDS MOTOR & THOROGHBRED & CLASSIC CAR SERIES

Motor & T & CC on Ferrari 1966-1976
Motor & T & CC on Ferrari 1976-1984
Motor & T & CC on Lotus 1979-1983

BROOKLANDS MILITARY VEHICLES SERIES

Allied Mil. Vehicles No.1 1942-1945
Allied Mil. Vehicles No.2 1941-1946
Dodge Mil. Vehicles Col. 1 1940-1945
Military Jeeps 1941-1945
Off Road Jeeps 1944-1971
Hail to the Jeep
US Military Vehicles 1941-1945
US Army Military Vehicles WW2-TM9-2800

BROOKLANDS HOT ROD RESTORATION SERIES

Auto Restoration Tips & Techniques
Basic Bodywork Tips & Techniques
Basic Painting Tips & Techniques
Camaro Restoration Tips & Techniques
Custom Painting Tips & Techniques
Engine Swapping Tips & Techniques
How to Build a Street Rod
Mustang Restoration Tips & Techniques
Performance Tuning - Chevrolets of the '60s
Performance Tuning - Ford of the '60s
Performance Tuning - Mopars of the '60s
Performance Tuning - Pontiacs of the '60s